A TRIBUTE TO MICHAEL FARADAY

SCIENTIFIC BIOGRAPHY

MICHAEL FARADAY. BY H. W. PICKERSGILL, R.A., 1830.
Presented to the Royal Institution by the Artist.

A TRIBUTE TO
MICHAEL FARADAY

By

ROLLO APPLEYARD

LONDON
CONSTABLE & CO LTD
1931

PUBLISHED BY

Constable & Company Limited
London W.C. 2

·

BOMBAY
CALCUTTA   MADRAS

Oxford University
Press

·

TORONTO

The Macmillan Company
of Canada, Limited

·

NEW YORK

Richard R. Smith Inc

PRINTED IN GREAT BRITAIN BY ROBERT MACLEHOSE AND CO. LTD.
THE UNIVERSITY PRESS, GLASGOW

Melodious falls the Sledge upon the Steel;
In rhythmic Glee the spark-lit Anvils shake.
Can Want and Toil from Strife such Music wake?
Has Earth a Joy to balance Pain, to seal
Affliction's myriad Pits, to mend, to heal—
Each Blow a Song, each Spark a Hope—to make
Less potent Grief, to stir numbed Minds to take
Forthwith the Will to act for Woe or Weal?
An Age ago, from London's midst there peered—
Recount it oft where Quests for Truth begin—
A Blacksmith's boy, one Michael, eagle-reared.
Distress-pursued, the Sun he sought to win
Along a Course he charted, sailed, and cleared;
Yet Michael Nature touched, and made the whole
    World kin.

R. A.

A HUNDRED years ago, Michael Faraday succeeded in "obtaining electricity from ordinary
magnetism." This led to developments whereby
electricity for lighting, heating, mechanical purposes, telegraphy, telephony, chemical processes,
and medical and surgical requirements, could
readily be generated, with consequent gain to all
humanity. His discovery he gave to the world
freely. The celebration of the event serves to remind us that, in addition to what he thus bestowed
that is tangible, he bequeathed his character, his
teaching, his example, and his ideals, of value beyond assessment. In tribute to his memory, what
is there that can transcend the results around us?
What can enhance the clearness, impressiveness,
and charm of his own writings? All our eulogy
is superfluous. The occasion, however, is appropriate for recounting the story of his parentage, his
environment, his mode of thought and operation,
his sympathies, his difficulties, his victories, and
his passion for truth.

For many of the illustrations and references it is
desired here to make acknowledgment to the
Royal Institution, to the Science Museum, South

Kensington, to the Institution of Electrical Engineers, to the Southwark Library, Walworth, and
to the authors quoted in the text. Thanks are
also given to the International Telephone and
Telegraph Corporation for permission to add
material intended for another purpose, but relinquished in favour of this. Gratitude must, moreover, be expressed to the Rev. Joseph A. Gorman,
Vicar of the Parish of Clapham (Yorkshire), for
allowing the church registers to be examined, to
the proprietors of *The Times* and the proprietors of
Punch for sanction to include extracts from their
columns, and to Mr. John Parker of Clapham
Wood farm, for his assistance in tracing what
remains of the Yorkshire homestead of the Faradays.

It is noteworthy that as James Clerk Maxwell,
to whom frequent reference is made in the text, was
born on June 13, 1831, and as the British Association held in that year their first Meeting, 1931 is in
a triple sense a centenary year for natural science.

R. A.

CONTENTS

LIST OF ILLUSTRATIONS

xii

LIST OF ILLUSTRATIONS

CHAPTER I

PARENTAGE

MICHAEL FARADAY, whose discoveries, whose teaching, and whose example, ennobled the days in which he lived, cast lustre upon all time. Each generation will reveal new aspects of his genius. John Tyndall, who was closely acquainted with him during the years 1850 to 1867, confessed that the preparation of the memoir "Faraday as a Discoverer" was "a labour of difficulty if also a labour of love." Bence Jones, the intimate friend, who wrote in 1870 *The Life and Letters of Faraday*, and who for thirty years listened to his lectures, declared that the task of producing that biography seemed, at first, hopeless. Other writers experienced like fears, and all have on that account left open the enticing path that is limitless.

The present generation may desire to know something of Faraday the man and the philosopher, and from his contemporary biographers to glean something of his name, his parentage, and his environment. With few exceptions the recorded personal

A

details concerning him are singularly devoid of coherence. Early in his life poverty stood at the gate; from middle age indifferent health impeded his steps. His career began in shadow; it ended like the going down of the sun. To interpret a little of what is known of him, to impart to it something of continuity, form, and meaning, to aid in establish∕ing what he was, what he did, and how he im∕pressed the world, the broken evidence must be associated with his scientific life, and it must be realised that the whole was sustained by high principles.

Bence Jones has recorded that the name "Richard ffaraday," stonemason and tiler, occurs in the parish register of Clapham (54.7 N, 2.24 W) in Yorkshire, and that this Richard died in 1741, a Separatist—a fact that may in some measure account for the difficulty of finding in church registers means to associate Richard's family with that of Michael.

The first ancestor of Michael definitely traced is Robert Faraday, born in 1728, who married in 1756 Elizabeth Dean of Clapham Wood Hall, Yorkshire, where between the years 1757 and 1773 these parents lived and had ten children. Robert died in 1786. The members of this family were

Sandemanians—a religious sect that afterwards had a church in London, to which Michael became attached.

Of the ten children of Robert there was one, James, born on May 8, 1761, who died in 1810. James, a blacksmith, married in 1786 Margaret Hastwell, born in 1764, who died in 1838—a farmer's daughter of Mallestang, near Kirby Stephen (54.29 N, 2.21 W) in Westmorland. Soon after their marriage James and Margaret made their home at Newington, near what was once the village of Walworth, in South London, where their son Michael was born on September 22, 1791. The site of the blacksmith's shop appears on a plan (Fig. 2), the date of which is about 1824. The street referred to as Cross Street on that plan is now Draper Street.

Where Cross Street met Newington Butts, in 1791, stood the parish church of St. Mary's, Newington. The term "butts" had existed since 1558, when butts were set up by royal mandate for the practice of archery. Traffic conditions in 1876, however, rendered it necessary to demolish this church for the widening of the highway. The registers were carefully transferred to a new church of the same name near Pentland Place, Newington

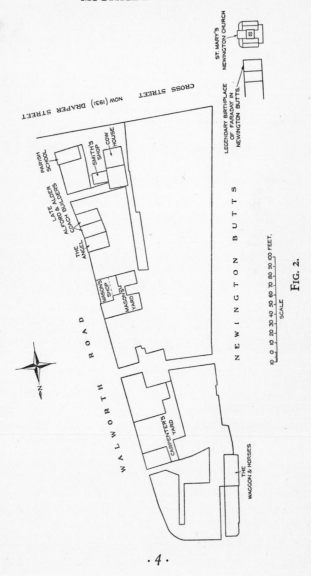

FIG. 2.

SKETCH OF ST. MARY'S, NEWINGTON. BY T. P. ALDER.
Presented to the Newington Free Library by the Artist.

Butts; but recent search there, and recent enquiry at Somerset House, have failed to identify the house where Michael was born. An idea of the character of the locality at the time of Michael's birth can be gathered from the sketches (Figs. 3 and 4). The unconfirmed local legend is that the blacksmith lived in one of the houses seen on the right of the church in those sketches.

The young family of James and Margaret:

Elizabeth,   born 1787,
Robert,   born 1788,
Michael,   born 1791,
Margaret,   born 1802,

suffered in the general distress of the time. In 1796, James, in ill-health, took his wife and the three little children to the North side of the Thames—to Gilbert Street, where he obtained rooms over a coachhouse in Jacob's Well Mews, Charles Street, Manchester Square. Michael, who was then five years old, found his playground in the streets in the neighbourhood of Spanish Place. Of his early education there is nothing known, except that it constituted little more than the rudiments of reading, writing and arithmetic at a local day school.

The fragmentary character of the particulars of

the childhood of Michael, that have been bequeathed to us by his contemporaries, suggested that an effort should be made to obtain additional evidence bearing upon his early environment. It was also desired to trace, if possible, the cause of the distress that fell upon his father and mother, and the reason that urged them to seek their fortunes in London. A recent visit to the Yorkshire homestead has revealed a few particulars in confirmation of the activities of the Faraday family.

Formerly, the parish of Clapham, near the borders of Yorkshire and Lancashire, embraced the townships of Clapham-cum-Newby, Lawkland, and Austwick. The *Parish Register* for that parish, for the years 1595-1683, was printed in 1921, at a time when Austwick formed a separate parish. This register contains no name of Faraday. There are entries in later registers in Clapham Parish Church (Fig. 5), but the most significant indications on the present occasion were at the farm on the site of what was once Clapham Wood Hall, nearly three miles from Clapham Parish Church.

The farm is reached by following the road that leads from Clapham railway station towards Slaid-

CONTEMPORARY SKETCH OF NEWINGTON.

burn, as far as a sign-post, where the road on the right—towards Bentham—must be taken. This is the Reebes Road. Continue along it, past a small church, to the stone bridge (Fig. 6a) that, at the bottom of the valley, crosses Keasden Beck. The farm-house (Fig. 6b) is then seen on the right. It is still called Clapham Wood House—a modest two-storied dwelling, built to some extent of the material of Clapham Wood Hall, long ago demolished.

Before following the path from the bridge to the farm-house note should be taken of the small detached building (Fig. 6a) on the right, that at this point fronts upon Reebes Road. The present owner of Clapham Wood farm, Mr. John Parker, through whose courtesy it has been possible to examine the estate, has discovered traces of a mill-race behind this structure. The building was once known as the "Home Barn"—and, in proof that it has served as a barn, it has walled-up openings for a "forking hole" and for a "shippon door," respectively. Documents in the possession of Mr. John Parker show, however, that in or about the year 1790 it was converted into what was described as a "Cotton Mill," and that at another period it was designated "the Bobbin Mill." Later it became a dwelling, and then a school. A deed confirms, in a note, that :

The Mill purchased by the Township was formerly a barn and converted by John Farraday the party to this deed into a cotton mill about 40 years ago.

The date of this note is somewhat indefinite, but it is probably 1832. Until about the year 1800 a good deal of hand-weaving was done in that part of Yorkshire. It is possible that the change from a "Cotton Mill" to a "Bobbin Mill" arose from a change of trade by the owners from weaving to bobbin-winding.

For further elucidation it is desirable next to leave the Bobbin Mill and to cross the meadow from it to the farm-house. This meadow has long been known as "Butt Garth" and, like Newington Butts, was probably used for archery. It will be observed that behind the farm house (Fig. 6b) the ground rises somewhat steeply. In stormy weather the old houses built without suitable protection upon this site suffered considerably from flood water. Re-building has therefore been necessary. The walls of the existing structure contain several relics of dressed stone from the ancient Hall, and one example of its foundations.

There is little doubt that, in the days of the

Faradays, two residences occupied this farm-house site, possibly under one roof, and that the family were closely associated with their neighbours, the Deans, before 1756, when Robert Faraday married Elizabeth Dean. In proof of this, the recent visit has revealed in the register of the parish church at Clapham the entry:

Thomas Farraday, Tiler, and Anne Dean, Spinster, both of the Parish of Clapham, and married by publication by the Revd Thomas Bowes, Vicar there, the first day of November 1740.

and the further item:

John Dean of Clapham Wood Hall (buried) April, 1756.

At the top of the hill that rises immediately behind the existing farm-house is another ancient barn, called the High Barn; it is built of stone, and is skilfully tiled. Leaning against its walls, on the outside, were recently (1930) two large flag-stones, resembling slate, from the Hellith Bridge "flag" quarry. The first of these bears marks "T.D. 1745; R.F. 1757; T.F. 1790." The second is also inscribed "R.F. 1757." The "R.F. 1757" corresponds to the birth of Richard, the slater and yeoman, eldest brother of James.

A human touch, that unites these dull objects,

is discovered in an Agreement, dated November 29, 1771, between Jane Dean of Clapham Wood Hall and John Farraday of the same place "second son of Robert Farraday." This

Witnesseth that for and in consideration of the natural love and affection which she bore for and towards him and for his further preferment in the world and for the sum of 5s/- of lawful money of England in hand well and truly paid before the sealing and delivery thereof . . . she the said Jane Dean did give . . . to the said J. Farraday . . . all the messuage and tenement standing and being at Clap-ham Wood Hall.

The document makes provision for the possi-bility that thereafter Jane Dean might marry; and a note in the margin asks:

Did Jane Dean Marry and had she issue?

The answer follows:

She married James Bickerstuff, but had no issue.

As Michael's uncle John, referred to in this agreement, was born in 1759, John received this gift upon the attainment of manhood. A deed, of May 31, 1756, referring to "Hannah Dean and Elizabeth Dean, two of the daughters of John Dean lately deceased," and to an agreement be-tween "Henry King, of Auswick" and Jane Dean

THE PARISH CHURCH AT CLAPHAM (YORKSHIRE).
From a snapshot by the Author in 1930.

of Clapham Wood Hall, is witnessed by Robert
Faraday, the grandfather of Michael.

From all this evidence it is to be inferred that the
resources of the two families were to a considerable
extent concentrated upon the weaving industry, and
that in or about the year 1790, when the mill was
sold to the township, trouble was approaching.
The end appears to have been reached ten years
later, for there is a deed of April 30, 1800, effecting
the "release of premises at Clapham Wood Hall in
the county of York by Richard Farraday and others
to Josias Physick for £380." It is signed:

Richard Faraday, yeoman. [Innholder, slater, grocer.]
John Faraday, weaver. [Farmer.]
James Faraday of the City of London, blacksmith.
Robert Faraday taylor of Bentham. [Packer in a flax mill.]
Betty Faraday, spinster. [Elizabeth.]
Jennet Faraday, spinster. [Jane.]
Hannah Faraday, spinster.
Thomas Faraday, cordwainer. [Kept a shop.]
Barnabas Faraday, cordwainer. [Shoemaker.]

They are described in the document as "the surviving sons and daughters of Robert Faraday late
of Clapham Wood Hall, yeoman." The document also refers to "Elizabeth Farraday, the widow
of Robert."

This agrees with the list of the children of Robert and Elizabeth, given by Bence Jones, except that William, who died in 1791, is absent. The differences from the Bence Jones list are for the present purpose added in parenthesis. Comparison of the lists of trades shows that John the farmer became a weaver, and that Robert, junior, the "taylor" became a packer in a flax mill. Thomas and Barnabas, the shoemakers, stuck appropriately to their lasts. It is to be observed that in 1800, nine years after the birth of Michael, his father James appears in the list as one of the nine concerned in the transfer of the Clapham Wood Hall premises. The share of the £380 would be but small—too insignificant to help him against the distress of the corn famine of 1801.

THE BOBBIN-HOUSE AND BRIDGE, CLAPHAM WOOD FARM.
From a snapshot by the Author in 1930.

CLAPHAM WOOD FARM.
From a snapshot by the Author in 1930.

CHAPTER II

THE THRESHOLD OF MICHAEL'S CAREER

AT thirteen, Michael entered the employment of Mr. Riebau, a bookseller, at No. 2 Blandford Street. So good a lad was he, and so prompt a newspaper boy, that, after a year's trial, his master accepted him, on October 7, 1805, as an apprentice—without premium—for seven years, to the trade of bookbinder and stationer. This shop is still in Blandford Street.

In 1809 the family removed to 18 Weymouth Street where, on October 30, 1810, Michael's father died. At the time of this calamity Michael served a worthy master and mistress, and he had advanced sufficiently to have two boy assistants. In Riebau's shop he was beginning to read the books as well as to sell them. Thus he was introduced to the study of the rudiments of chemistry and electricity; and he made simple experiments.

Between the years 1810 and 1811 he attended lectures at 53 Dorset Court, Fleet Street. These were generously paid for by Michael's brother, Robert, at a shilling a lecture. At about this time also he obtained, by good fortune, lessons in drawing and perspective from Masquerier—a fact that accounts for the quality of his more carefully drawn representations of apparatus and of other objects.

On October 8, 1812, his apprenticeship being at an end, he entered as a journeyman bookbinder, the service of Mr. De La Roche, a French emigrant —a man of acid temper who caused Faraday much annoyance. The youth became restless. This unsatisfactory condition of affairs was, however, soon to be altered; for, amidst his troubles, the lure of natural science was already indicating the direction of his career.

He had been taken, in February, March, and April, 1812, by Mr. Dance, one of the customers at the book-shop, to hear on four occasions Sir Humphry Davy at the Royal Institution; and in December, 1812, he ventured to write to the lecturer offering his services as an amanuensis. His letter was accompanied by notes, admirably put together and bound, of the four lectures. The volume is now in the archives of the Royal Institution. The reply, received on December 24, 1812, was more than encouraging, for Davy recognised the effort as an example of zeal, power of memory, and attention, and he signified his wish to see the young man early in the new year.

The result of the interview was that on March 8, 1813, Faraday—now twenty-two years of age—was appointed as an assistant in the Laboratory of the Royal Institution, at a salary of 25s. a week, with two rooms in which to live at the top of the house.

Faraday, as a youth, and indeed throughout his life, was intensely studious, but he was neither dull nor ascetic. A certain degree of adversity imparted qualities that prosperity might have denied to him. To a friend he wrote at this time with the utmost cheerfulness:

I shall be at Ranelagh to-morrow evening, and if we do not meet before, will take up my stand exactly at nine, under the orchestra.

Again, he confided to this friend:

There is a grand party at dinner at Jacques Hotel, which immediately faces the back of the Institution, and the music is so excellent that I cannot for the life of me help running, at every new piece they play, to the window to hear them. . . . Listen, listen, to the voice of the bassoons, violins, clarionets, trumpets, serpents, and all the accessories of good music.

Here too is his confession:

I keep regular hours, enter not intentionally into pleasures productive of evil, reverence those who require reverence of me, and act up to what the world calls good.

Friendship he already regarded as "one of the sublimest feelings of which the human mind is capable."

Day by day, at this stage of his career, he realised the need for self-education, and especially he regretted his ignorance of foreign languages. His industry had led him from the desert of poverty to the edge of a wilderness. There he had a vision of what was to be accomplished, but he was without the means, as yet, either of penetrating to the depths or of clambering to the heights. The Royal Institution promised wealth of instruction in natural science. London—to those who knew its resources as he did—offered ways of acquiring mastery of other subjects. He resolved to school himself in what he lacked. Circumstances, however, suddenly arose that modified if they did not destroy his plans. Fate gave him a chance, which he readily took, to become a graduate of the vast university of Europe—for in 1813 Sir Humphry Davy asked him to accompany him and Lady Davy, with her maid, upon continental travels.

CHAPTER III

THE GRAND TOUR

DAVY in 1813 obtained safe-conduct to visit enemy countries. Historians may well consider whether it would be more correct to ascribe this to the astuteness or to the magnanimity of Napoleon. It must suffice to remind ourselves briefly of what, in essential details, was then the condition of Europe. At the time of the birth of Faraday the absolute monarchy of Louis XVI that had displaced feudal monarchy in France was itself overthrown. The French people, crushed by poverty and taxation, cried for bread and for revenge. Sedition spread. War followed, in which France, successful against her external enemies, was almost overwhelmed by internal strife; until, in October 1795, Bonaparte stemmed the tide and brought momentary cessation to the revolution. The victories that placed him in command of the Austrian Netherlands, his advance through the Tyrol and the Northern part of Italy, his threat to descend upon England, his ultimate campaign against Malta, Egypt, and Syria, his position when he encountered Austria and

Russia on land, and the British Fleet at sea, his brilliant counter attacks that led to the truce of 1801-1802, are familiar history.

At the time of the renewal of war in 1803 Bona-parte held as prisoners 10,000 visitors who happened to be in his territory. By October, 1804, he had ready an army of 150,000 troops for an attack upon England. Then came Austerlitz and Trafalgar, and in 1806 the Confederation of the Rhine, followed by the Peninsular war, and in the winter of 1812-1813 his fatal retreat from Moscow. The drama did not cease, however, until 1815, the year of Waterloo and of the Second Peace of Paris. Into such a Europe did Sir Humphry Davy and his party enter for their Grand Tour.

From the record that Faraday has left of this ex-pedition it is possible to appreciate the infelicitous character of some of the personal tasks that fell to him. He says:

When Sir Humphry Davy first made proposals to me to accompany him in the voyage, he told me that I should be occupied in assisting him in his experiments, in taking care of the apparatus, and of his papers and books, and in writing, and other things of this kind; and I, conceiving that such employment, with the opportunities that travel-ling would present, would tend greatly to instruct me in what I desired to know, and in things useful in life, con-

sented to go. Had this arrangement held, our party would have consisted of Sir Humphry and Lady Davy, the lady's maid, Le Fontaine (Sir H.'s valet), and myself; but a few days before we came off, Le Fontaine, diverted from his intention by the tears of his wife, refused to go, and thus a new arrangement was necessary. When Sir H. informed me of this circumstance, he expressed his sorrow at it, and said he had not time to find another to suit him (for Le Fontaine was from Flanders, and spoke a little Italian as well as French), but that if I would put up with a few things on the road, until he got to Paris, doing those things which could not be trusted to strangers or waiters, and which Le Fontaine would have done, he would there get a servant, which would leave me at liberty to fill my proper station and that alone. I felt unwilling to proceed on this plan; but considering the advantages I should lose, and the short time I should be thus embar-rassed, I agreed. At Paris he could find no servant to suit him, for he wished for one that spoke English, French, and a little German (I speaking no French at that time), and as all the English there (ourselves excepted) were prisoners, and none of the French servants talked English, our want remained unsupplied; but to ease me he took a lacquais de place, and living in an hotel, I had a few things to do out of my agreement. . . . As I am the person in whom Sir Humphry trusts, it obliges me to take a more active share in this part of my present occupation than I wish to do; and in having to see after the expenses of the family, I have to see also after the servants, the table, and the accommodations.

I should have but little to complain of were I travelling with Sir Humphry alone, or were Lady Davy like him; but her temper makes it oftentimes go wrong with me, with herself, and with Sir H. . . .

Finally, Sir H. has no valet except myself; but having been in an humbler station, and not being corrupted by high life, he has very little occasion for a servant of that kind, and 'tis the name more than the thing which hurts.

In fairness to Davy it must be remembered that Faraday had not yet risen above the horizon. It was impossible, in 1813, for the professor to know the precise level or aspirations of his assistant. Never, theless, it is easy to comprehend with what bitter, ness Faraday observed the grotesque parallelism— lady and maid, master and valet.

The reference to the task of "taking care of the apparatus" on these travels awakens curiosity con, cerning the luggage that was put into the carriage that conveyed the strangely assorted four across Europe. The biographer of Davy tells us that the means of experimenting, whilst on the Continent,

Were comprised in the contents of two small boxes . . . one 20 inches long, 7 wide, and 4 high, used for holding tests—the other 12 inches long, 7½ wide, and 6 high, for holding instruments, as glass tubes, small receivers, re, torts, and capsules, a blow, pipe apparatus, a small pneu, matic trough, a delicate balance, and a few other necessary

. 20 .

articles. The balance . . . was constructed entirely of platina and agate—the knife-edge, and other parts subject to friction, of the latter material—the rest, of the metal . . .

Davy's view of a scientific expedition was that "all the implements absolutely necessary may be carried in a small trunk," and he gave proof of this. Only occasionally, in particular researches, did he have recourse to the well-appointed laboratories of Florence and Rome.

In the Library of the Institution of Electrical Engineers, London, there is Faraday's own journal of the first part of this tour beginning on Wednesday, October 13, 1813. There is the entry:

This morning formed a new epoch in my life. I have never before, within my recollection, left London at a greater distance than twelve miles, and now I leave it, perhaps for many years, to visit spots between which and home whole realms will intervene.

They drove from London at about 11 a.m., and they slept the night at Amesbury. The next day they crossed Salisbury Plain, concerning which Faraday records that

During our progress we saw at a distance the singular structure of Stonehenge but did not go to see it, Plymouth being the point of attraction which had most force at the time.

Late that evening they arrived at Exeter. On

October 15 they reached Plymouth in the afternoon, and Faraday confesses, "I was more taken by
the scenery to-day than by anything else I have ever
seen." They had intended to cross at once to
Morlaix, but the wind was adverse, and did not
moderate until Sunday (October 17). They then
proceeded on board the cartel, a small vessel which
was to take them across the English Channel, but
"much delay occurred with the Jewish money
changers." He regretted this, as darkness set in
and he missed "the receding view of Plymouth."
During the night-passage, however, he had "a fine
opportunity of observing the luminescence of the
sea." He was a good sailor and enjoyed the voyage.
Incidentally, they sighted a French privateer. They
arrived outside Morlaix too late on Monday,
October 18, to enter the port, but the next day they
got ashore and collected the various parts of their
travelling carriage, their boxes and their packages.
After a somewhat severe ordeal of examination
they obtained, on Friday, October 22, liberty to
leave the town, and they travelled at night as far as
Guingamp. It was here that Faraday exclaimed:
"This evening I for the first time saw a glow
worm!" A few days later his admiration was
whetted again; this time by the French pigs—with

their long thin bodies, backs arched upwards, lank sides, long slender feet—which were capable "of outrunning our horses for a mile or two together."

On Sunday, October 24, they advanced towards Paris by way of Rennes, which they left the next morning for Laval, Alençon, and Versailles. His first impression of Paris was disappointing. He writes: "I know nothing of the language or of a single being here, added to which the people are enemies. . . . I must exert myself to learn their language so as to join in their world."

Considering the circumstances of the time, the French were exceedingly generous, for on November 9 the members of the party were given passports. He was amused to find himself described in his document as the possessor of "a round chin, a brown beard, a large mouth, and a great nose." This gave him entrance to all public museums and libraries on any day of the week, although the public were admitted to many of them on but two or three days of the week. On November 18 he had the misfortune to lose the passport; but, much to his relief, it was found again on the following Saturday. On Tuesday, November 23, he is in company with Ampère and others, examining a new substance—iodine.

On Sunday, December 19, 1813, he remarks:

This is an important day. The Emperor has just visited the Senate in full state. The weather has been very bad, but that did not prevent me and thousands more from going to see the show. . . . [The Emperor] was sitting in one corner of his carriage, covered and almost hidden from sight by an enormous robe of ermine, and his face was shaded by a tremendous plume of feathers that descended from a velvet hat. The distance was too great to distinguish the features well, but he seemed of a dark countenance and he seemed corpulent. His carriage was very rich, and fourteen servants stood upon it in various parts. An enormous crowd surrounded him. The Empress and a great number of courtiers followed in other carriages. No acclamation was heard where I stood, and no comments.

This may be compared with the account in *The Times* of December 24, 1813:

To-day, Sunday, December 19, His Majesty the Emperor and King set off at one o'clock from the palace of the Thuilleries, to repair in state to the Legislative Body, where, having been received with the usual ceremonies, His Majesty, after taking his seat, made [a] speech . . . After the speech, the Session being terminated, His Majesty rose in the midst of acclamations. His Majesty returned to the palace of the Thuilleries, with his retinue. . . .

In Faraday's journal there are very few sketches,

but there is one where, in referring to Paris in December, 1813, he describes, with admirable conciseness, the Chappe mechanical telegraph:

On looking over Paris from the hill of Montmartre, a number of telegraphs catch the eye, some of which are always moving in the day time. They are very different to the English telegraphs, being more perfect and simple. A strong upright supports on the top a movable cross beam, at the ends of which are two others; but the arms of these, though the same in length and weight, are not so in make—one arm of each piece being merely a rim of wood weighted, and at a distance is lost to the sight. Small wheels are fixed on the axes, which of course move with the arms; ropes pass over them and down the sides of the upright into the chamber below, and by their means the parts are moved and put into different positions. About 250 figures, each perfectly different from the others, and easy to be distinguished, can be formed by this instrument.

After a residence of three months in Paris the party left on December 29. Of the gay city Faraday carried with him rather sombre thoughts; but on that frosty morning, as they entered the Forest of Fontainebleau, he was cheered by a scene which he admitted was more beautiful than anything he had ever before witnessed. Every visible object was resplendent in a garment of wonderful airiness and delicacy. It was upon this occasion that Davy wrote his poem on Fontainebleau.

They slept at Nemours, and proceeded early the next morning along the road to Moulins. At 5 a.m. the moon had set, and they made their way by starlight along the banks of the Loire, the waters of which at times came to their horses' feet. On December 30, about fifteen minutes after sunset, he witnessed for the first time "the phenomenon called the zodiacal light." He describes it as an emanation in enormous rays from the sun into the expanse, continuing for about half an hour.

The next day they travelled through the snow, and "to lessen as much as possible the labour of the poor tired post horses" the party alighted and walked for some miles through wild vales and passes. Then, as a variant of Sterne's *Sentimental Journey*, they arrived late at an inn and were "turned out of bed by the hostler at 3 a.m." At Lyons on Sunday, January 2, 1814, they found several English families as prisoners. Faraday remarks that the town was guarded only by a dozen muskets. On January 5 they left Lyons with post horses at 9 a.m., and travelled by the side of the Rhone towards Avignon. He now obtained a glimpse of the Dauphiny Alps, and at last Mont Blanc appeared to him "as an enormous insulated mass of white rocks." They slept at Vallence, and proceeded on January 6, 1814, along the Rhone track.

At Pont d'Esprit they crossed the Rhone, and on Friday, January 7, they saw the Roman aqueduct, at Languedoc. They passed on through Nimes, where they examined the amphitheatre, and on Saturday, January 8, 1814, they reached Mont- pellier. Two days later they visited Peyrou, where there was "good red wine at 3d. a bottle (English) and another very much less." Fuel was expensive, and "was sold in packets, fifty pounds for thirty sous." At Montpellier on February 1, 1814, " the town was all in an uproar and running to see the passing of a battery of artillery . . . going up to- wards Lyons . . . in great haste."

When it is remembered that Faraday was an Englishman in hostile territory, it is remarkable that on February 3 he walked unmolested beyond the fortifications. On February 5 he wrote:

Drilling is now the occupation of the town, and Peyrou looks like a parade. During the morning it is covered by clumsy recruits who are endeavouring to hold their arms right, turn their toes out, keep their hands in, and hold their heads up, according to the direction of certain corporals who are at present all authority and import- ance.

His account for Sunday, February 6, mentions that:

The Pope passed through this place a few days ago on his way to Italy; he has just been set at liberty . . . they say he was received in a very pathetic manner, and with a multitude of sighs, tears and groans.

The party left Montpellier on Monday, February 7, 1814, once more for Nimes. The journal describes the Roman remains in such detail as to indicate that if Faraday had not surrendered to chemistry and physics he would have been a precise and illuminating antiquarian.

They left Nimes on February 8. He was again much impressed by the Alps, and particularly by Mont Ventoux. They returned to Avignon, crossed two arms of the Rhone, and saw the former palace of the Popes. With three horses now to their carriage they proceeded to Aix, and on the way observed for the second time the zodiacal light "in great perfection."

From Aix they reached Frejus; two days later they crossed the Var, and on February 16 they arrived at Nice. As they advanced towards the Alps excitement was caused by a report that robbers had been on the road the day before. Moreover, a dwelling along the road was on fire. Faraday remarks that "the manner of extinguishing it was very philosophical, and, if it could be applied properly, very efficacious; it was to exclude air from the fire and suffocate it by covering up every crevice."

His journal is from its novelty attractive. He restricts his observations mainly to things. Concerning people he is too often silent—though he met on this journey some of the most remarkable men of his time. He was still little more than a youth. The tour is concisely described in the letters of Sir Humphry Davy.

According to Davy it was intended to be "a journey of scientific inquiry." They were to go rapidly through France, Italy, Sicily, and Germany, with every assurance from the Governments that the party should not be molested, but assisted. Davy explains that he was provided with a commodious portable apparatus for instituting such inquiries as he had in contemplation, and he confirms that in Paris he determined the nature of iodine—a substance discovered two years before by Curtois. He then relates that they visited the Auvergne to examine extinct volcanoes, and Montpellier to resume inquiries on combinations of iodine. They remained in Genoa a few days for experiments upon the torpedo fish, and to examine marine productions for iodine. On March 18, 1814, Davy wrote:

I ... passed from the Pyrenees to the Alps, twice crossed the Apeninnes, visited all the most remarkable extinct volcanoes in the South of France ... met Ampère and Gay Lussac ... lived very much with Berthollet, Cuvier, Chaptal, Vauquelin, Humboldt, Morveau, Clement, and Chevreul. ... At Florence more than a fortnight ... afterwards Rome ... [examined the] nature of the diamond and of the different varieties of carbon ... quitted Florence at the beginning of April for Rome ... remained in Rome nearly a month ... Naples about three weeks.

Again, it is Davy that tells of the visit of the party to Volta:

Volta I saw at Milan, in 1814, at that time advanced in years—I think nearly 70, and in bad health. His conversation was not brilliant; his views rather limited, but marking great ingenuity. His manners were perfectly simple. He had not the air of a courtier, or even of a man who had seen the world. Indeed, I can say generally of the Italian savants, that though none of them had much dignity or grace of manner, yet they were all free from affectation.

Faraday entered in his diary the date of this visit, June 17, 1814, with the bare remark:

Saw M. Volta, who came to Sir H. Davy, an hale elderly man, bearing the red ribbon, and very free in con-versation.

From Milan they crossed the Alps by the Sim-plon Pass, and they arrived at Geneva in the last week of June, 1814. At Geneva, as Tyndall re-cords in the *Dictionary of National Biography*, they were the guests of Davy's friend De La Rive, father of the celebrated electrician. In this private house the difficulties of social status became acute— especially in the case of Lady Davy:

Host and guest were sportsmen, and they frequently went out shooting. On these occasions Faraday loaded Davy's gun, and for a time he had his meals with the servants. From nature Faraday had received the warp and woof of a gentleman, and this, added to his bright in-telligence, soon led De La Rive to the discovery that he was Davy's laboratory assistant, not his servant. Some-what shocked at the discovery, De La Rive proposed that Faraday should dine with the family, instead of with the domestics. To this Lady Davy demurred, and De La Rive met the case by sending Faraday's meals to his own room. Davy appears to have treated Faraday with every consideration. He sometimes brushed his own clothes to relieve his assistant of the duty, but Lady Davy was of a different temper. She treated Faraday as a menial, and his fiery spirit so chafed under this treatment that he was frequently on the point of returning home. . . .

They remained in Geneva until September, 1814, and thence they passed to Italy, through the Tyrol, for the winter in Rome.

Application was at this time made by them for passports for the Turkish Empire, with residence in Constantinople. It was Davy's intention to travel amongst the Greek islands in March, and to be at Athens early in the Spring of 1815.

Faraday was not enthusiastic about the prospect, but meanwhile he was entering into the "mirth and jollity of the Carnival amongst the Romans." On January 30, 1815, he went in a domino to a masked ball, where he found much amusement. The ball was held in a theatre, the stage and pit of which were thrown together by a flight of steps. He remarks:

The pit was good for waltzing, and the stage for cotillon and country dances. . . . A crowd of soldiers in the house preserved order, and a gentleman in black with a cocked hat sat in the centre box and overlooked the whole. . . . There was much masking in the Corso, and the sugar plums . . . were now flying in the air. These confetti, as they are called, are merely plaster or old mortar broken into small pieces and dropped in a mixture of whiting. . . . None but masks are allowed to throw, though this rule is transgressed from every window. . . .

The English were much more eager at this sport than

the Romans. . . . On my way to the Academy I made a great blunder—I mistook a burial for part of the mas-querade. The sackcloth coats were very similar to what the masked clowns and punchinellos wear; their enormous knotted cords tied round their waists, their sandals, and their caps, like a brewer's straining bag, with two little holes for the eyes, were as complete a mask as it is possible to make; and it was not till by chance I saw the body that I thought it was a serious affair.

In March, 1815, they left Rome for Naples and studied Vesuvius. Their intention then was to travel East, but they were deterred by rumours that the plague had broken out in Malta and in the Levant. They therefore returned to England by way of the Tyrol. On this occasion they avoided France by making a detour through part of Ger-many and Flanders. According to Davy, they embarked at Ostend, landed at Dover, and arrived in London on April 23, 1815.

CHAPTER IV

MICHAEL DISCOVERS HIMSELF

FARADAY was happy to return. The tour had made a deep impression upon him. It was no small thing to have traversed France, Italy, Switzerland, Germany, and Flanders, to have been in touch with the leaders of thought and science, to have observed natural phenomena on the grand scale, to have climbed the Alps, to have looked upon Na-poleon in all the panoply of imperial state, and to have been guided throughout by a philosopher of the knowledge, skill, and renown of Davy. Hard-ships had been encountered, pride had suffered, the normal course of life had been broken; but lessons beyond price had been learned, and there were days of happiness to be remembered. He had been es-pecially in his element in the city of Florence. In Rome he had entered fully into the fun of the Car-nival—in night-cap and night-gown. Moreover, the tour had set him up in health and spirits—for, as he wrote to his mother shortly before his return, he had become "heavier and thicker," he had toasted "Old England," and he had sung "God save the King" and "Rule Britannia" on Vesuvius.

What were his thoughts as he returned to Albe-marle Street and entered once more the portals of the Royal Institution? His correspondence shows that in the Autumn of 1814 there had been doubt concerning the continuance of that establishment. The reason for these misgivings is not stated, but probably the Managers were confronted by ques-tions of ways and means. A hint of this is given in the "Personal Remembrances" of Sir Frederick Pollock, where credit is given to the Rev. John Barlow, for many years Secretary to the Royal In-stitution, whose

> . . . exertions had been of immense use in rescuing it from a position of serious financial difficulty, and [whose] constant attention to its interests much assisted in main-taining its efficiency and popularity.

Apart, however, from surmise, and apart from any desire Faraday may have entertained to free himself from anything approaching menial service, there was a more potent reason, for there was a good chance that he might take up residence for some years in Italy, to carry out researches upon the papyri of Herculaneum.

The facts concerning this project were explained in a Paper read by Sir Humphry Davy before the

Royal Society on March 15, 1821. It will suffice here to remind ourselves that Herculaneum, near Naples, was overwhelmed by an eruption of Vesuvius in A.D. 79. The ruins were discovered accidentally by the sinking of a well in 1713. Amongst many other objects were found innumerable manuscripts consisting of rolls of papyrus in various states of injury from age, agglutination, and mutilation. Sir Humphry applied his chemical knowledge to the task of enabling them to be unrolled and rendered legible. With the assistance of the Museum staff at Naples he succeeded in unrolling twenty-three of the manuscripts, but for adequate reasons he then abandoned the task. The Roman manuscripts were in general composed of papyrus of thicker texture than those of Greece. The writing was judged to belong to the schools of the Epicurean philosophers and sophists. It was contemplated that Faraday would be suited to the task of continuing the work, but, fortunately for natural science, the negotiations collapsed.

On May 7, 1815, two weeks after his return to England, Faraday became an Assistant at the Royal Institution, in what was termed the "Laboratory and Mineralogical Collection." He was also appointed Superintendent of the Apparatus. During the next few years, in addition to his work for the Royal Institution, he had a certain amount of private employment. A glimpse of his life between the years 1815 and 1820 is to be obtained from a letter to his friend Abbott in April, 1819.

On Monday evening there is a scientific meeting of members here, and every other Monday a dinner, to both of which my company is requested. On Tuesday evening I have a pupil, who comes at six and stops till nine, engaged in private lessons. On Wednesday, the Society requires my aid. Thursday is my only evening for accidental engagements. Friday, my pupil returns and stops his three hours; and on Saturday I have to arrange my little private business.

Now you will see that except on Tuesday and Friday after nine, I have no evening but Thursday for anything that may turn up.

It is stated by Dr. J. H. Gladstone that one of the first tasks undertaken by Faraday at Albemarle Street was to put in order the mineralogical collection. He was also occupied in extracting sugar from beetroot, and in preparing bisulphide of carbon and the explosive chloride of nitrogen. It was with this explosive that he and Davy were injured. When he was not engaged with the lectures he was manufacturing rare chemicals or performing analyses. Chlorine had for him fascination. "He investigated its combinations with carbon, squeezed it into a liquid, and applied it successfully as a disinfectant when fatal fever broke out in the Millbank Penitentiary." Again he is seen "trying to harden steel, and prevent its rusting, by alloying it with small quantities of platinum and of rarer metals. A boy blew the bellows till the crucibles melted, but a few ordinary razors seemed to have been the best results."

It was his custom on Saturdays to visit his mother and his sisters. He was subjecting himself to a severe course of self-education in English "composition, style, delivery, reading, oratory, grammar, pronunciation and perspicuity." Notwithstanding these endeavours he experienced at that time difficulty in presenting his ideas in happy sequence.

I always find myself obliged, if any argument is of the least importance, to draw up a plan of it on paper, and fill in the parts by recalling them to mind, either by association or otherwise; and this done, I have a series of major and minor heads in order, and from these I work out my matter. Now, this method, unfortunately, though it will do very well for the mere purpose of arrangement and so forth, yet it introduces a dryness and stiffness into the style of the piece composed by it; for the parts come together like bricks, one flat on the other, and though they may fit, yet they have the appearance of too much regu-

larity. . . . I would, if possible, imitate a tree in its pro-
gression from roots to trunk, to branches, twigs, and leaves.

The earliest of his own lectures was at the City
Philosophical Society, 53 Dorset Street, Salisbury
Square, on January 17, 1816—on "The General
Properties of Matter." Later in that year he gave
six further lectures on cohesion, chemical affinity,
radiant matter, oxygen, chlorine, iodine, fluorine,
hydrogen and nitrogen. He continued in 1817, the
eleventh being on September 3, on "Combustion."
The twelfth was on October 15, on "Metals."

In 1817, at the recommendation of Davy, Faraday was selected to give private lessons in miner-
alogy and chemistry three times a week, for a few
months. Nevertheless, he continued in 1818 his
course of lectures at the City Philosophical Society.
In particular, there was one on " Observations on
the Inertia of the Mind " that displays considerable
expansion of his ideas.

From time to time during these years he sought
relaxation in the country. In January, 1817, he
visited Barnstaple to recover his health after an accident. In July, 1819, he made an excursion into
Wales and kept a journal in which he showed appreciation of beautiful scenery, and considerable power
in describing it.

His status in the world of science was rapidly rising.

There was, however, some uncertainty in his tenure at the Royal Institution; for, early in February, 1819, Davy communicated with him from Rome, concerning the Herculaneum documents:

I have sent a report on the state of the MSS. to our Government, with a plan for the undertaking of unrolling; one part of the plan is to employ a chemist for the purpose at Naples; should they consent, I hope I shall have to make a proposition to you on the subject.

In May, 1819, he received from Davy, who was then at Florence, a letter expressing good fellowship and encouragement:

It gives me great pleasure to hear that you are comfortable at the Royal Institution, and I trust that you will not only do something good and honourable for yourself, but likewise for science.

I am, dear Mr. Faraday, always your sincere friend and well-wisher,
                                                   H. DAVY.

The experience he had gained in lecturing at the City Philosophical Society, and the severe schooling to which he had subjected himself in elocution, brought the reward that by 1820 he was an accomplished speaker. Moreover, by his work in the laboratory, he had developed into a skilful experi-

FARADAY'S SPECIFIC INDUCTIVE CAPACITY APPARATUS.
From a photograph by the Science Museum, South Kensington.

FARADAY'S SPECIMENS OF HEAVY GLASS.
From a photograph by the Science Museum, South Kensington.

menter. Nevertheless, he had not yet solved all the problems that life presented. At the Sandemanian Church there was an Elder, Mr. Barnard, a silver‐smith of Paternoster Row, whose third daughter, Sarah, disproved all the arguments that Faraday had urged against the ruling passion. He wrote to her from the Royal Institution, confessing that she had converted him from his erroneous theories. Her mother, wise and of prompt action, withdrew Sarah to Margate "in order to postpone any im‐mediate decision." Faraday followed within a few days, and arranged with Miss Barnard an excursion to Dover, where—to use his own phrase—he was "blessed with success." On August 7, 1820, he returned to London and wrote to Sarah that although he wanted to say a thousand heartfelt things to her, his mind was in a quandary of stupid‐ness, chlorides, trials, oils, Davy, steel, and fifty other fancies. They were married on June 12, 1821.

As the relationship between Sir Humphry Davy and Faraday has occasionally been regarded as lacking that spirit of friendship and consideration which ought to have united them, it is pleasant here to observe, what indeed is manifest in many other parts of this history, that Davy, with few exceptions, behaved well towards him. Faraday wished to make a home for himself and his wife at the Royal Institution. What transpired between him and Davy is not recorded, but on March 11, 1821, Davy wrote :

DEAR MR. FARADAY,

I have spoken to Lord Spencer, and I am in hopes that your wish might be granted; but do not mention the subject till I see you.

In May, 1821, Faraday was appointed Super-intendent of the House and Laboratory at the Royal Institution. In 1823 he was still acting as Davy's "chemical assistant." In the Spring of that year he had the misfortune to injure his eyes as the result of an explosion. He records that:

It was from one of my tubes, and was so powerful as to drive the pieces of glass like pistol shot through the window. However, I am getting better, and expect to see as well as ever.

CHAPTER V

KING WILLIAM IV INTERVENES

THE following year was marred by a note of dis-cord in his relations with Davy. All that need here be observed is that any reproaches that may have been thought or said disappeared when the facts were presented in their true light. In confirmation of his having passed through this ordeal un-scathed there is the fact that in January, 1824, he was elected a Fellow of the Royal Society. The completeness with which friendly relations were restored is indicated by the circumstance that on February 7, 1825, Davy informed the Managers of the Royal Institution that he considered the talents and services of Mr. Faraday, Assistant in the La-boratory, were entitled to some mark of approbation from the Managers. These sentiments met with cordial concurrence, and it was resolved "that Mr. Faraday be appointed Director of the Laboratory under the superintendence of the Professor of Chemistry."

Faraday at once invited the members of the Royal Institution to come to evening meetings in the

Laboratory, and in 1826 he inaugurated those Friday evening meetings that were destined to become famous.

His first course of six lectures in the Theatre of the Royal Institution began in April, 1827, the subject being Chemical Philosophy. As the provision of this Lecture Theatre was a great help to the activities of the Institution, it is appropriate to consider how and when it came into existence.

Lately there have been discovered the Articles of Agreement, dated June 12, 1800, between the Proprietors of the Royal Institution and a Contractor, Thomas Hancock of Pimlico, for additions, alterations, repairs, and improvements to the premises in Albemarle Street, for the sum of £5227. The structural work was to be completed by January 1, 1801, and the whole by March 1, 1801. These Articles were signed on behalf of the Institution by Claudius Stephen Hunter and by George Saunders. The agreement relates to new buildings containing the "workshop, repository, lecture room, and connected parts." On the plans the interior of the Lecture Theatre is shown "43 feet $10\frac{1}{4}$" from back to front, about 62 feet from side to side, and 30 feet from floor to ceiling. The pit was designed for eleven rows of seats on the slope, with an addi-

tional row in front on the floor level. The gallery
was designed for three rows of seats. The lecture
table was to be 12 feet long and 2 feet 6 inches wide.
Faraday had a table of different design (Fig. 8). The
front of the whole building was to be brick. It is

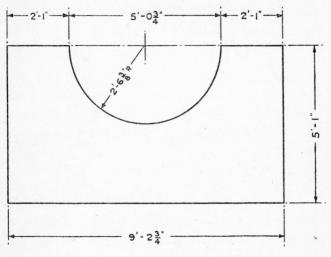

THICKNESS $1\frac{3}{8}''$

FIG. 8.

Plan of Faraday's Lecture Table. From dimensions taken
by the Author while it was being dismantled in 1929.

to be inferred that these preparations were in antici-
pation of the lectures of Dr. Thomas Young and of
the beginning of the dynasty of Davy at Albemarle
Street. The colonnade (Fig. 9), did not exist at that
time—it was designed in 1831 by Lewis Vulliany,

· 45 ·

and it has some resemblance to the Tempio di Antonino Pio in Rome (Fig. 10). The name of the architect of the Lecture Theatre does not appear on the plans of 1801, and is not mentioned in the contract; the following letter, the result of a search through Faraday's correspondence, throws some light upon the matter:

41 London Street,
Fitzroy Square,
23rd May, 1836.

DEAR SIR,

    It was but the other day I learned that you had mentioned me in your evidence before the Committee of the House of Commons on the subject of the Theatre of the Royal Institution. I immediately referred to the Report of the Committee in your library, and found that I had been rightly informed.

    I write now, therefore, to thank you for having done me justice in stating that I was the architect. The whole of the principles by which I was guided in forming the design, together with many circumstances relating to its execution which have contributed towards that degree of perfection of which you was so kind as to speak, I really believe, from the various examinations I have read in the reports, and the designs which I have lately seen exhibited, are yet known only to myself.

        I am,
           Dear Sir,
           Your much obliged hum^{ble} serv^{t},

To Michael Faraday, Esq.   *THOS. WEBSTER.*

THE ROYAL INSTITUTION (1929).

Dr. J. H. Gladstone has referred briefly to the Royal Institution as it was in the days of Faraday, with its Lecture Room capable of seating 700 persons, with its Laboratory, and with its Froggery —a part of the Laboratory so called from a tradition that frogs had once been kept there.

As the part played by Sir Humphry and Lady Davy is essential to the story of Faraday, it is appropriate here to introduce some account of them. Humphry, who was born in 1778, was the son of Robert Davy, a wood-carver of Penzance, who had married Grace Millett of the same county. Robert and Grace were of good family, but of no great wealth. Early in life Humphry was befriended by John Tonkin, a surgeon of Penzance, who sent him to a preparatory school, and who afterwards persuaded Humphry's father to transfer the lad to Penzance Grammar School. Later, the young scholar went to Truro, for Latin and Greek. His school and college education was completed at fourteen. In 1794 his father died, and the next year Tonkin apprenticed Humphry to John Bingham, a surgeon. As in the case of Oersted, it was in the apothecary's dispensary that he was attracted to chemistry and to experiments. His means were very limited; consequently his apparatus consisted chiefly of phials, wineglasses, tea cups, tobacco pipes, and earthen crucibles.

Like Volta he had a bent for literature, and a struggle soon took place to determine whether he would become poet or philosopher—and philo-sophy prevailed. He was acquainted with Davies Giddy—who afterwards was famous as Gilbert Davies—at whose recommendation he obtained in 1798 an appointment as Assistant Superintendent to the Pneumatic Institution at Bristol.

The next year Davy visited London for the first time, and in consequence of the distinction gained as the result of his researches in chemistry he was appointed, in 1801, Assistant Lecturer in Chem-istry, Director of the Chemical Laboratory, and Assistant Editor of the Journals at the "Institution for Diffusing Knowledge"—which afterwards be-came the Royal Institution—at a salary of £100 per annum. His subsequent early success and popu-larity were remarkable, but he survived flattery. He became President of the Royal Society.

In 1808 he was awarded the Napoleon prize of Frs. 3000 "for the best experiment made on the galvanic fluid." He advised the British Govern-ment, in 1811, on the ventilation of the House of Lords. In 1812 he was knighted by the Prince

THE TEMPIO DI ANTONINO PIO (ROME).
From an engraving in the possession of the Author.

Regent, and on April 11 of that year he married Mrs. Apreece, a Scottish widow. One of his biographers remarks that thereafter he became more aristocratic, for "he discovered charms in rank which had before escaped him."

He invented, in 1815, the safety lamp, but was troubled by the counter claims of Dr. Clanny and of George Stephenson. Three years later he was made a Baronet. His discoveries, researches, and writings placed him in the forefront of the world of science. He came under influences, however, that led him, to his loss, to seek ascendancy also in the world of fashion. In April, 1813, he resigned his professorship of the Royal Institution, but he was appointed Honorary Professor of Chemistry. In 1827 he resigned the Chair of the Royal Society. His health had already failed, and on May 29, 1829, he died.

His wife, Lady Jane Davy (1780-1855), was the only daughter of Charles Kerr, a younger son of William Kerr, of Kelso, Scotland. Her mother was Jane Tweedie, who died in 1796. Lady Jane was first married in 1799 to the eldest son of Sir Thomas Hussey Apreece, who died in 1807. Jane, now a widow—young, wealthy, and of advanced views—survived the bereavement, and went to Edinburgh,

where her drawing-room became the meeting place
of the cleverest and brightest of that capital. It is
said of her that she was attractive by the vivacity of
her conversation, and that her parties gained for a
time a mastery over all others. As a result, on April
11, 1812, she took Sir Humphry Davy as her
second husband. She is described as small, with
black eyes and hair, a very pleasing face, an un-
usually sweet smile, a brunette of the brunettes, or,
as Sydney Smith more concisely expressed it,
"brown as a dry toast." Whatever may have been
her virtues they were impaired by the vice be-
tokening her mediocrity, for "she liked to show her
authority, and to mortify her husband's companion
(Faraday)."

What part, if any, did she play in instigating the
tour, and in obtaining permission from Napoleon
for the two philosophers to cross to the hostile continent in October, 1813? The inquiry is speculative,
but it throws instructive light upon the world of
politics and fashion into which fate thrust Faraday.
Lady Davy claimed acquaintance with Madame
de Staël, an erudite but lovable sentimentalist, who
was banished from Paris by the Emperor Napoleon.
Madame de Staël, after many wanderings, visited
London in May, 1813, and she became at once the

centre of attraction. Lord Byron complained that "the polished horde were never tired of staring at her." Amongst other diversions, this adventuress carried on innocent correspondence with the Emperor's brother Lucien Bonaparte, who in 1813 was a prisoner at Thorngrove in England. A letter from Lucien to her, dated July 5, 1813, can be seen amongst the Foreign Office records. To combine these facts into a plot would be easy, but is no part of the present purpose. The search reveals no trace of the negotiations that gave Faraday his passport. Amongst the treasured documents in the Record Office, however, is one that tells of the kind of craft—a cartel—in which the party crossed the English Channel. It is a letter dated November, 1813, granting permission to bring into this country a considerable amount of property belong⁄ing to "Mr. De Humboldt, consisting of books and prints now in france [with a small ' f '] to be despatched by cartel from Morlaix." The vessel was to be one or other of the following:

Brilliant, 50 tons. William Roach, Master.
Hawke, 40 tons. John Bagges, Master.

In June, 1829, a few weeks after the death of Sir Humphry Davy, Faraday accepted a lectureship at the Royal Military Academy, Woolwich. To trace his mode of life at about that time there is no better guide than Bence Jones. Faraday was fond of entertaining his friends at the Royal Institution. After dinner they played like boys. In all such games Faraday was generally victorious. Sometimes he ran round the Theatre of the Royal Institution on a velocipede, "which was then (1830) a new thing." Occasionally the merry party went up the river Thames in a rowing boat to picnic. They were fortunate to include in their company the singers Garcia and his wife and daughter. Faraday at this time was acquainted with "all the best Italian singers . . . and most of the Royal Academicians, including Stanfield, Turner, Westall, and Landseer." In the world in which Faraday moved supper parties were followed by charades, at which Faraday took part with Garcia, Malibran and the rest. Among the artists, Faraday appears to have been more intimately acquainted with Turner, who applied to him for information concerning pigments. On the other hand, Faraday made observations upon the effect of light and vapours upon tints and washes.

His happiest days were when he went sketching with his wife. He was not, as Davy had been, a fisherman—he preferred geologising or botanising, music, and swimming. In contrast, it may be observed that he was occasionally in the laboratory by nine o'clock in the morning, and that he remained at work there until nearly eleven at night. He found rest in reading a story or a novel. His special enjoyment was when, on rare occasions, he took his wife to the theatre. They usually walked there and sat in the pit. His friends provided him for some seasons, however, with free admission to the opera.

The velocipede was not used by Faraday solely for exercise round the Lecture Theatre of the Royal Institution—it often took him early in the morning for a run to Hampstead. Another of his amusements was his flute, and also singing. Dr. J. H. Gladstone records that Faraday "sang bass correctly, both as to time and tune."

To obtain an impression of Faraday during the years 1830 to 1840 it is best to refer to the account of him for that time given by his niece, Miss Reid. She sees him hard at work on experiments connected with his researches—"his apron full of holes." Young ladies of early Victorian times were, in the next era, credited with having been useful with needle and thread, but to her uncle's apron

Miss Reid does not appear to have applied her skill. She continues that "if he was very busy he would merely give a nod," whereupon her aunt would sit down quietly with her in the distance. Presently he would make a note on his slate, and would turn round to have a talk; or he would go upstairs with them to finish the evening at bagatelle, stipulating for a half-hour's work first to finish his experiment. When he was dull and dispirited, as sometimes he was to an extreme degree, her aunt used to go with him to Brighton or somewhere else for a few days, and they generally came back refreshed and invigorated. Often of an evening they would go to the Zoological Gardens. He was diverted by the tricks of the monkeys. Miss Reid says—"We have seen him laugh till the tears ran down his cheeks as he watched them." Further, he never missed seeing the wonderful sights of the day—acrobats, tumblers, giants and dwarfs; even a Punch and Judy show was an unfailing source of delight to him, whether he looked at the performance or at the admiring, gaping crowd.

By the year 1835 Faraday had gained great distinction. His lectures and, above all, his discoveries had made his name famous. In July, however, he was suffering from fatigue and rheumatism, and although he had promised himself never again to leave England, he made a tour in Switzerland. It was on this occasion that he renewed and deepened his friendship with De La Rive. He returned from Switzerland on August 6, 1835, to take up again the question of electro-chemical decomposition, but he still felt very tired and could not get up his energy.

Here he was passing the zenith of his activities. He was now not merely a master of natural philo-sophy—but a man of affairs, in contact, upon occasion, with the leaders of social and political life. Between us and his time there intervenes a century of European history that obscures, if it does not obliterate, the world in which he lived. To restore something of the outline it is necessary to observe a few of the phantoms that trail across the mists. First comes King George IV, who died without surviving issue, on June 26, 1830. He was suc-ceeded by his brother, the Duke of Clarence, then sixty-five years of age, who became William IV. On June 20, 1837, William IV died, and as he had no surviving child the crown passed to Victoria, daughter of his deceased brother Edward, Duke of Kent. Meanwhile, in France—after the abdication, in 1815, of the Emperor Napoleon—Louis XVIII took up government under the protection of the allies. Louis XVIII died in 1824, and was succeeded by his brother Count d'Artois, who became Charles X, and abdicated in 1830 in favour of the Duke of Bordeaux. The French rejected the Duke of Bordeaux, and placed Louis Philippe, Duke of Orleans, upon the throne. Louis Philippe died in 1848. Louis Napoleon, son of Louis Bonaparte, tried in 1836 to depose Louis Philippe. Louis Napoleon was arrested, however, and was sent to America; but he returned to Europe, and from about 1837 to 1840 he resided in England. After a career of peril, he again took refuge, in 1846, in England. In 1848 he was elected President of the French Republic.

The encouragement given by Louis Philippe to the cause of telegraphy deserves to be remembered. It was referred to by Mr. Brett—at the historic banquet given to the chairman and directors of the Atlantic Telegraph Company in September, 1858 —who recalled that, in 1845, when a proposal was made to Sir Robert Peel, who was then at the head of the Government, to unite England and France by a telegraph cable, if Government assistance could be afforded, Mr. Brett was directed to call at the Admiralty Office. He did so, but all the offers he made were rejected. He then applied to Louis Philippe, King of the French, for assistance, which under certain restrictions was at last granted. (*Vide The Observer*, September 12, 1858.)

The Reform Bill of 1831 and 1832 was passed through the House of Commons, but was twice rejected by the House of Lords. There were consequent riots throughout England, following upon which the Bill was accepted by the Lords, and it received the Royal assent. In October, 1834, the Houses of Parliament were destroyed by fire. In the following month King William dismissed his Ministers and sent for Sir Robert Peel, who was at that time in Rome. Sir Robert Peel formed a Cabinet, and issued a manifesto. King William opened Parliament on February 24, 1835. The Commons, however, never forgave the King for dissolving the previous Parliament; Peel's Ministry was consequently defeated, and on April 8, 1835, Lord Melbourne became Premier.

Early in 1835, the Premier, Sir Robert Peel, had decided that, as a mark of distinction, Faraday ought to receive a pension from the State. Subversion of Sir Robert Peel's Government, in April, 1835, unfortunately occurred before the arrangement could be put into effect. The result was that

Faraday and his pension were caught in the political machinery between Whig and Tory, with very painful consequences. His friend, Sir James South, acted as adviser with good effect, and the matter ended creditably to all concerned.

In *The Times* of Saturday, November 28, 1835, there appeared a statement, extending for nearly a column, on "Tory and Whig Patronage to Science and Literature," being an extract, here reprinted by kind permission of the proprietors of *The Times*, from an article in *Fraser's Magazine* for December, 1835. It began by saying that

Among other bitter Whigs who receive pensions from Sir Robert Peel, on the ground of scientific eminence, may be particularized Professor Airy and Mr. Dalton. We may say nothing of Mrs. Somerville, for a lady's politics go for little; and the lady in question well deserves to find favour in the eyes of men of all parties. But Sir Robert Peel found it impossible, during his brief tenure of office, to complete the circle which he had begun. He was therefore compelled to draw up an official document, in which were inserted the names of certain persons to whom it had been his intention to extend the Royal bounty, with a particular statement of the amount of pension which had been designed for each. Among these, the name of Faraday was entered, with an intimation that he ought to be placed on an equal footing with Professor Airy, by giving him a pension of £300 a year.

This minute of Sir Robert Peel's apparently was passed on to Lord Melbourne, and Melbourne resolved to begin with Faraday. Now Faraday could not otherwise be distasteful to the Whig Premier, than that his merits had chanced to attract the notice of Sir Robert Peel. . . . Accordingly, the Liberal Prime Minister commenced operations with an attempt to put off Mr. Faraday with a pension less in point of value by one-third than that which the Tory had promised. . . . Tom Young was commissioned to sound Faraday's confidential friends to ascertain from them whether he would consent to accept £200 a year. To this the reply was prompt and peremptory: It is not the value of the pension that is regarded; but the position which it marks for the pensioned in the ranks of science. Mr. Faraday shall not accept a pension inferior to that which has been bestowed upon Professor Airy.

Then followed an account of an interview, real or imaginary, by Tom Young with Faraday, and an interview still more striking between Lord Melbourne and Faraday, ending with a refusal by Faraday to accept any favour at his hands—for Lord Melbourne "grossly insults the first chymist of his day, for no other reason than because he chanced to have attracted the notice of Sir Robert Peel."

The dénouement was remarkable. Soon after these incidents, Lady Mary Fox chanced to visit Sir James South, on whose table she saw a small electrifying

machine with a ticket on it indicating that "The machine
... is the first of which Faraday ever came into possession." It stood when he was a youth in an optician's
window in Fleet Street, and was offered for sale at the cost
of 4s. 6d.; yet such was the low state of Faraday's
finances that he could not purchase it. Many a day he
came to the window to gaze, and went away again bitterly
lamenting his own poverty, not because it subjected him to
bodily inconvenience, but because it threatened to exclude
him for ever from the path of science and usefulness, on
which he longed to enter. At last he did succeed in purchasing it, and he had now presented it to Sir James South.
Lady Mary was greatly touched by this simple tale, she
highly approved of the reply that Faraday had made to
Lord Melbourne. The whole story was repeated to the
King, including an outline of Faraday's early struggles
with poverty, and the Monarch was so affected by the
narrative that he shed tears; "that man deserves all the
pension that Peel promised," said the King, "and he shall
have it too." So Lord Melbourne is informed that, whatever his Lordship's feelings might be, those of William the
Fourth are the feelings of a gentleman. And Faraday is,
after all, to accept the pension—not as a gift from the Whig
Cabinet, but directly from the King.

Faraday did not contradict this story, but on
Tuesday, December 8, 1835, he wrote to The Times
begging leave publicly to state that neither directly
nor indirectly did he communicate to the editor of

Fraser's Magazine the information on which that article was founded, or further, either directly or indirectly, any information to or for any publica/ tion whatever.

CHAPTER VI

LIFE'S TALE MADE UP

IN 1837 and 1840, for reasons of failing health, he was obliged to reduce the daily amount of time bestowed upon original research. In 1841 he was troubled with loss of memory and giddiness to such an extent that he had to take rest. Accompanied by his wife and his brother-in-law, he again went to Switzerland. His journal of the tour, beginning on January 30, 1841, and ending on September 29, 1841, is preserved.

Later, he forced himself to do a little work for Trinity House, and he began his Juvenile Lectures at the Royal Institution at Christmas. In 1843 he suffered much from depression. The year 1844 was not remarkable for original research, but he was speculating on the nature of matter, and was developing his ideas concerning physical lines of force.

An independent opinion upon him at this time is to be found in the *Life, Letters, and Journals of Sir Charles Lyell*, the renowned geologist. The two men were brought together in the course of an

MICHAEL FARADAY. BY M. NOBLE.
Presented to the Royal Institution by William Bowman, Esq., F.R.S.

investigation of a terrible disaster that occurred on Saturday, September 28, 1844, at Haswell Colliery, in the county of Durham, when ninety-five lives were lost. All England was stirred, and the Premier, who was then again Sir Robert Peel, decided to request a geologist and a chemist to visit Haswell. Accordingly, Faraday and Sir Charles Lyell attended the coroner's inquest, with the object of enquiring into the causes of the explosion, and if possible to suggest means of preventing the recurrence of such catastrophies. The two philosophers arrived on the scene on Tuesday, October 8, 1844. They first examined the Davy lamps, and found some bruised and bent, some with holes torn in the gauze, and one with signs of fire on the lower half of the gauze as if gas had been burning against it. They discovered that men could light a pipe from a Davy lamp of the pattern in use, and, although smoking was strictly forbidden, cases had been known of men smoking in the mine. It was in the bad old days when young children were employed in the mine—one of the lamps had in fact belonged to a boy of ten or twelve years of age. Sir Charles Lyell was very much struck by the quickness with which Faraday, on this occasion, as a commissioner, transformed himself from a man of science into an astute cross-examiner. It may be remarked, however, that Faraday had from his youth been a student of evidence. In one of his early note-books is written the dictum:

Testimony is like an arrow shot from a longbow; the force of it depends on the strength of the hand that draws it. Argument is like an arrow shot from a crossbow, which has equal force though shot by a child.

He disliked "doubtful knowledge." His concern was with the truth, apart altogether from prejudice. For those who abused their prerogatives, for those who sought to influence opinion or judgment by asserting their ascendancy, he had nothing but contempt.

At the inquest Faraday asked how they measured the rate at which the air flowed in the mine. By way of answer an inspector took a small pinch of gunpowder out of a box, as he might have taken a pinch of snuff, and allowed it to fall gradually through the flame of a candle which he held in the other hand. His companion, with a watch, marked the time the smoke took to go a certain distance. Faraday asked where they kept the powder. They said they kept it in a bag, the neck of which was tied up. "But where," said he, with insistence, "do you keep the bag?" "You are sitting on it" was the reply. They had in fact given this—the most yielding seat available—to the commissioner.

From that time the acquaintanceship between Sir Charles Lyell and Faraday continued, and in February, 1848, the geologist gave a lecture at the Royal Institution on "The Reptiles in the Coal Formation of the Alleghenies," concerning which he wrote to his sister:

Before lecture, Faraday pleased me by some hints, and showing me his private memoranda for lectures, and telling me what I suspect he hardly ever did to anyone, part of his mechanism for timing the different parts. It is wonderful how I had come by practice to the same results. He has given fifty or a hundred lectures to my one, and is the chief master of the art in England, to my mind. The number present as noted down at the entrance, was 398, but it may have been more, as Mr. Barlow does not quite trust the new porter. . . .

Faraday's health improved in 1845—the year in which he discovered what was at first called "the magnetisation of light"—and he was able in May, 1846, to communicate to the *Philosophical Magazine* his famous article "Thoughts on Ray Vibrations."

Whatever pleasure he may have derived from those successes, however, was marred by a heavy loss; for his brother, when driving, was upset and was so injured that he died on August 13, 1846.

E

In the summer of 1847 Faraday complained of failure of memory, confusion of ideas, and giddiness. Later in the year his doctors advised him to give up working, and he took their advice. Subsequently he returned to his researches, but in the early part of 1848 he did but little in the Laboratory.

Brighter days followed, for in 1849 he was again giving discourses at the Royal Institution, and in 1850 he carried out a good deal of original research. Prince Albert at this time was attracted to him, and at the end of 1851 an invitation was received to visit His Royal Highness at Windsor in order that they might have some conversation on the magnetic properties of oxygen.

Submarine cables were now being closely investigated. In 1852 Faraday experimented at the works of the Electric Telegraph Company, on submerged insulated wires of great length. He published a paper in the *Philosophical Magazine* on this subject, he gave a lecture upon it at the Royal Institution, and he communicated an account of his experiments in this direction to De La Rive.

In 1858 Queen Victoria, in the kindliest and most gracious manner, desired that he would take up his residence in one of Her Majesty's houses on

Hampton Court Green, near London. This he did. When Her Majesty heard of his extreme weakness, she gave commands for his living rooms to be arranged on one floor, without steps. His friend, Thomas Twining, designed for him a special wheel chair, which is now a relic at the Athenaeum.

In 1864 Faraday, still at Hampton Court, was a weary man. He relinquished his work, and in 1865 he wrote more cheerfully to his friend Tyndall. But towards the end of that year he had an attack of illness from which he never completely rallied. Tyndall says that complete rest now became essential, and that "slowly and peacefully he sank towards his final rest, and when it came, his death was a falling asleep." He died on August 25, 1867, at Hampton Court, and he was buried on August 30, 1867, at Highgate Cemetery.

It is appropriate here to dwell somewhat upon his influence, and upon the impressions he left in the minds of those about him.

A charming aspect of him revealed itself in a letter he wrote to his friend Tyndall on October 6, 1855. Tyndall had been perturbed by one of those personal difficulties that occasionally arise between men of science and the governing body of an institution—on this occasion the British Association.

Faraday was sympathetic and expressed his sorrow that Tyndall should have been caused annoyance. He solaced Tyndall with gentle words:

Let me, as an old man, who ought by this time to have profited by experience, say, that when I was younger I found I often misinterpreted the intentions of people, and found they did not mean what, at the time, I supposed them to mean, and further, that as a general rule, it was better to be a little dull of apprehension where phrases seemed to imply pique, and quick in perception, when on the contrary they seemed to convey kindly feelings. The real truth never fails immediately to appear, and the opposing parties are, if wrong, sooner convinced when replied to forbearingly than when overwhelmed. All I mean to say is, that it is better to be blind to the results of partisanship, and quick to see good will. One finds more happiness in oneself in endeavouring to follow the things that make for peace. You can hardly imagine how often I have been heated in private when opposed, as I have thought, unjustly and superciliously, and yet I have striven and succeeded, I hope, in keeping down replies of the like kind.

Dr. J. H. Gladstone, who was a personal friend, has recorded some pleasant incidents in the life of the great philosopher. Here, for example, is part of the letter that Faraday, when established in his career, wrote to his former master, Mr. G. Riebau, the bookseller:

Not used to the arts of flattery, I can only express my obligations in a plain but sincere way. Permit me therefore, Sir, to return thanks in this manner for the many favours I have received at your hands and by your means, and believe me, your grateful and obedient servant,

MICHAEL FARADAY.

The intensity with which he could focus upon the results of his experiments, and the ingenuity with which he could develop them in order to resolve doubts and difficulties, had occasional contrasts in mental stress, anxiety, depression, or ecstasy. In 1854 he was able to write to Tyndall :

Our subjects are so glorious, that to work at them rejoices and encourages the feeblest; . . . enchants the strongest.

Tyndall adds: "A good experiment would make him almost dance with delight."

There are, as Faraday once observed, plenty of portraits of him, but not a single likeness. It was his principle not to help to publish portraits of himself; nevertheless there exist enough to guide posterity. Tyndall remarks that Faraday was below the middle height, well set, active, and with extraordinary animation of countenance. His head was exceptionally long; his hair was naturally curly and brown, until late in life when it approached to white. His voice was pleasant, his laughter hearty, and he possessed wonderful vivacity. Artists and sculptors vied with one another to convey something that sprang from the nobility of mind and the kindly heart of this great Englishman.

A list of the learned societies to which he belonged, numbering seventy-two, and distributed throughout the world, is appended to Dr. Gladstone's *Michael Faraday*.

Sir Frederick Pollock, in *Personal Remembrances*, has an entry in his diary for August 25, 1867:

On this day died Faraday, a great and good man gone.

To this tribute may be added that of Lady Pollock in *St. Paul's Magazine* for June, 1870:

[Michael Faraday] could not be too closely approached. There were no shabby or ugly corners in his mind. The ascendency of his genius was the more complete because of the virtues which were developed with it. . . . He was indifferent to the distinctions usually coveted by genius . . . not having that love of glory—or as it is sometimes called in speaking of other nations, that vanity—which takes delight in adding lustre to the illustrious.

Lady Pollock alludes also to his constant consideration for others, the simplicity of his life, his admirable control of temper, his true modesty, his skill in lecture experiments. At supreme moments in those lectures:

His body then took motion from his mind. His hair streamed from his head. His hands were full of nervous action. His light, lithe body seemed to quiver with its eager life. His audience took fire with him, and every face was flushed . . . each hearer shared his zeal and his delight . . . [By] the sincerity of his manner . . . his vivacity, and his pleasant laugh . . . he won the confidence of children. They felt as if he belonged to them. He was like an inspired child.

His lecture table was always in such perfect order that everything was to hand at the right moment. Instruments were so placed as to be never in his way. Manipulation never interfered with his discourse. Lady Pollock refers also to his enthusiasm, which sometimes carried him to the point of ecstasy, and to his irresistible eloquence compelling attention so that "it waked the young from their visions and the old from their dreams." He was, she adds, "the true man for the juveniles—all was done with a natural impulse."

No man was ever so ready to give his time and service to his country; none ever did so much for love, so little for reward. Our daily life is full of resources which are the results of his labours; we may see at every turn some proof of the great grasp of his imaginative intellect. Remembering the achievements of his genius, we may look for future revelations of nature's truth with boundless hope. . . . It must excite actual veneration, and a deep sense of gratitude for such an example of excellence . . . to kindle enthusiasm in minds capable of aspiring after the things which are great and good.

This old friend also tells of an incident that does infinite credit to Faraday's sense of what was due to the memory of a departed warrior from the field of science. She remarks:

On one occasion, when some allusion to his early life from a friend brought on the mention of a painful passage between himself and Sir Humphry Davy, he rose abruptly from his seat . . . and said: "Talk of something else, and never let me speak of this again. I wish to remember nothing but Davy's kindness."

Lady Pollock observed in Faraday a certain resemblance to Lord Nelson, and she refers to his "peculiar, ironical humour," that was light, genial, pungent, but entirely free from the bitterness of satire.

His lecture at the Royal Institution on December 27, 1855, was an occasion of importance. His Royal Highness Prince Albert attended with the Prince of Wales (afterwards King Edward VII)

FARADAY LECTURING AT THE ROYAL INSTITUTION ON DECEMBER 27th, 1855.
From a painting by Alexander Blaikley.

and with Prince Alfred (the Duke of Edinburgh). The scene was sketched by Alexander Blaikley, and was afterwards painted by him. It was reproduced in the *Illustrated London News*, and it was regarded as "gratifying evidence of the care bestowed upon the early education of the Royal Family in thus introducing them to the culture of the higher branches of knowledge. The picture (Fig. 12) represents Faraday giving the first of a Course of Juvenile Lectures, on "Metals." The Prince Consort is in the Chair, and his sons are on either side of him. Near him in the front row are shown Sir Charles Fellowes, General Sir Frederick Pollock, Mr. Barlow, and Dr. Bence Jones.

Contemporary reports of his lectures confirm that impression of his qualities. Here, for example, is an account from *Punch* of March 14, 1857. It is to be found amongst "Mary Ann's Notions"—a serial commentary of current events, supposed to be addressed to the Editor of that journal by a fashionable young lady of Victorian tastes. This extract is reprinted by permission of the Proprietors of *Punch*:

Do you know Dr. Faraday? I suppose so, as you know all the clever people in the world. Isn't he a dear? We went, that is Lizzy Hamerton and her brother

Charles, and Augustus and me, to the Royal Institution the other night, and Dr. Faraday gave a lecture. Prince Albert was there with his Star on, looking so grave and elegant; and by the way, I do wish that you would not have ridiculous pictures made of him; for he is excessively good looking still, and I dare say much handsomer than any of you folks that caricature him. He listened with the utmost steadiness, and I do not believe he moved half a quarter of an inch all the time. They set him in a great chair, you know, exactly in front of the lecturer. . . . But the lecture was lovely. It was quite a treat to look at dear Dr. Faraday's earnest face and silvery hair, not that he is an old man, far from it, and he is far more light and active than many a smoking stupid all-round collar man that I know. . . . Here was Dr. Faraday, a really great man, diving into the wonderful secrets of nature, and explaining them in the ablest manner. Where were all the great men and statesmen, and the M.P.'s and all those who pretend to lead the world? Listening to him as he unfolded these mighty things? Not they.

His more intimate thoughts, his restrictions, aspirations, and guiding principles are revealed in a letter to his friend Lady Lovelace, who suggested the repetition of some of his experiments. This letter is still among the treasures in the Library of the Institution of Electrical Engineers. It is dated October 24, 1844.

I am constrained to a continual process of lessening my

intentions and curtailing my pursuits. Many a fair dis-covery stands before me in thought which I once intended and even now desire to work out, but I lose all hope re-specting them when I turn my thoughts to that one which is in hand, and see how slowly for want of time and physical power it advances, and how likely it is to be . . . only a barrier between me and the many beyond.

. . . Those physico-mental faculties by which the mind and body are kept in conjunction and work together, and especially the memory, fail me, and hence a limitation of all that I was once able to perform. This has had a great effect in moulding portions of my later life [and] has tended to withdraw me from the communion and pursuits of . . . some of my contemporaries.

. . . Religious conversation is generally in vain. There is no philosophy in my religion. I am of a very small and despised set of Christians known, if known at all, as Sande-manians, and our hope is founded on the faith that is in Christ. But though the natural works of God can never by any possibility come at contradiction with the higher things that belong to our future existence—and must with everything concerning Him ever glorify Him—still I do not think it at all necessary to tie the natural sources of religion together, and in my intercourse with my fellow creatures that which is religious and that which is philo-sophical have ever been two distinct things.

CHAPTER VII

ADVOCACY OF SCIENCE IN PUBLIC SCHOOLS

TO take up one by one the relics of his correspondence, and to learn at how many points he was in touch with the affairs of his time, is to realise that his keen perception and his generosity of mind exerted, upon the leaders of thought and action, powerful influence. To illustrate this it will suffice to recall that on November 18, 1862, he gave evidence before the Public Schools' Commission, consisting of the Earl of Clarendon, the Earl of Devon, Lord Lyttleton, Sir Stafford Northcote, Hon. Edward Twisleton, Rev. W. H. Thompson, and H. Halford Vaughan. In answer to their questions he explained that for twenty years he was an Instructor for the Government at Woolwich:

Professor of Chemistry there, or Lecturer on Chemistry, I should rather say, because the Professorship passed away with Mr. Culloch, and was not renewed until I left. I am also one of the Senate of the London University—one of the original nominees. I am not an educated man, according to the usual phraseology.

He complained that the teaching of science had —as a matter of habit and prejudice—been almost completely overlooked in the Public Schools. Science, he told the Commission, is now knocking at the door.

I know very little of the Public Schools. . . . Men of science, fit to teach, hardly exist to-day. There is no demand for such men. Life is so short. The sciences make up life. They are important to life. The highly educated man fails to understand the simplest things of science, and has no peculiar aptitude for grasping them. I find the grown-up mind coming back to me with the same questions over and over again.

He complained that the public schools had not even attended to knowledge of how to write legibly, and he continued:

A multiplicity of subjects efface each other. [The object of education should be] to train the mind to ascertain the sequence of a particular conclusion from certain premises, to detect a fallacy, to correct undue generalization, to prevent the growth of mistakes in reasoning. Everything in these things must depend on the spirit and the manner in which the instruction itself is conveyed and honoured. If you teach scientific knowledge without honouring scientific knowledge as it is applied . . . you do more harm than good. You only discredit both the study and the parties concerned in it. . . . I never yet found a boy who was not able to understand by simple explanation, and to enjoy the point of an experiment. I do think that the study of natural science is so glorious a school for the mind, that with the laws impressed on all these things by the Creator, and the wonderful unity and stability of matter, and the forces of matter, there cannot be a better school for the education of the mind. Persons who have had the discipline of classical instruction . . . persons who have been fully educated by the present system . . . are ignorant of their ignorance at the end of all that education. That happens with men who are excellent mathematicians. Until they know what are the laws of nature, and until they are taught by education to see what are the natural facts, they cannot clear their minds of absurd inconsistencies.

He was asked whether the knowledge that could be presented in a school for acquisition could be made the subject of examinations, so as to test the proficiency of pupils, and to enable the examiners to state their order of merit one above another according to their attainment and ability. It is to be observed that he did not support this vicious system—the bane of educational life. He replied "I have no doubt of it." He urged the necessity for teaching Natural Science, and he bore witness to the fact that the opposition and prejudice to that form of education were breaking away. He referred especially to the useful purpose served by

science in such matters as provision of lights at sea.
He said:

*I have had occasion to go over to France with a deputy
board and to look at their lighthouses, and we find intelli-
gent men there whom we cannot get here. In regard to the
electric light, which you may have heard of, we have had
to displace keeper after keeper for the purpose of getting
those who could attend to it intelligently.*

*I trace everything to the ignorance of the learned in
literature as often as the unlearned, and their want of judgment in natural things . . . where often there is a fine
intellect in other things . . . they want the ABC of
science, and not the XYZ . . . they want the first elements. The ordinary schoolmaster does not know it.*

*I must not shut out mathematics; mathematics, as it
seems to me, is the only part of actual knowledge which
the general system of education at present takes in. It is
the one thing in which the literary man touches applied
science. . . . The term "training of the mind" has for
me a very indefinite meaning. . . . What does mind learn
by that training? To be attentive, to be persevering, to be
logical. But does it give that training of the mind which
enables a man to [assign] a reason in natural things for
an effect which happens from certain causes? It is the
highly educated men that we find coming to us again and
again asking the most simple question in chemistry or
mechanics. . . . I find their minds deficient [though] not in
their own studies.*

Who are the men whose powers are really developed?

Who are they who made the electric telegraph, the steam engine, and the railroad? Are they the men who have been taught Latin and Greek? Are they Stephensons? . . . I have never had an opportunity of learning that kind of knowledge from the schools. . . . You want a man who can teach, and there is that class to create . . . gradually bringing in the love of this kind of knowledge, and opportunity for it. . . . In fact it comes to this, an experimental mode of advancing knowledge. . . . I would teach (the little boy of ordinary intelligence) mechanics, hydrostatics, hydraulics, pneumatics, acoustics, optics—and chemistry.

Lectures depend entirely for their value upon the manner in which they are given. It is not the matter, it is not the subject, so much as the man. Teachers have never recognised its value, and it obtains for nothing in the schools. It obtains no marks. . . . [His plea was for that other knowledge which language only helps to describe.]

He told the Commission that although he advocated the teaching of natural science he was not opposed to teaching classics. He drew their attention to the keenness of the school boys and school girls who attended his lectures—how they came rushing up to his table to ask questions and to see the experiments—and he observed, "those who like it best come first, and they so crowd round the lecture table as to shut out the others." In his view, in the order of instruction, chemistry should take precedence; but his "chemistry" included elec⁄tricity and magnetism.

In addition to what he accomplished in the laboratory and in the lecture room, Faraday was plied with questions from every quarter. Without any of the modern means to facilitate writing, the task of furnishing replies was heavy upon him, and often distressing. There exist certain of his letters to and from leading men of science, disconnected memoranda, commonplace books, requests for information and advice, and a full measure of those wearisome epistles that the natural inclination ot the average man neglects, and that only courtesy supreme, as possessed by Faraday, could notice. To⁄day these relics reveal the quality of his mind, the sympathy of his touch, that alone could reduce complexity to order. His plan was to select, to co⁄ordinate, and to publish all that appertained to the advance of chemistry and physics.

CHAPTER VIII

EXPERIMENT AND MATHEMATICAL ANALYSIS

THE mind of Faraday, clear and penetrating, was also in the highest degree imaginative. Discipline to which he subjected himself in his studies and in his experimental work, produced in him a power of logical reasoning that enabled him to interpret physical actions and to describe them in terms free from mathematical expressions. Nevertheless, as the century following him has revealed, his discoveries and the principles he deduced from them were essential to the subsequent development of electricity, magnetism, and optics as a single mathematical science. He tells us that he felt bound to let experiment guide him into any train of thought it might justify, "being satisfied that experiment, like analysis, must lead to strict truth if rightly interpreted." He believed experiment to be far more suggestive of new trains of thought and "of new conditions of natural power" than is mathematics. He declared that, without experiment, he was nothing.

Contrasts and similarities between his methods of investigation and those of the mathematicians deserve attention. His published works and his correspondence indicate that, although he was not himself advanced in that branch of learning, he placed mathematics high in the order of importance of subjects taught in the public schools of his time. His attitude towards it was that of a skilled warrior who, while preferring his own sword, recognises the advantage of each weapon selected by other men for an encounter. In the *Philosophical Transactions* for 1852 he says:

Just as either geometry or analysis may be employed to solve correctly a particular problem, though one has more power and capability, generally speaking, than the other, or just as either the idea of the reflexion of images, or that of the reverberation of sounds, may be used to represent certain physical forces and conditions, so may the idea of the attractions and repulsions of centres, or that of the distribution of magnetic fluids, or that of lines of force, be applied in the consideration of magnetic phenomena. It is the occasional and more frequent use of the latter which I at present wish to advocate.

It is to be remarked that the production of lines of iron filings by sprinkling the particles over glass or paper above a magnet did not originate with Faraday. His genius interpreted them as lines of force, and he proceeded therefrom to imagine physical lines, or tubes, communicating stress from one part of a medium to another, with corresponding pressures at right angles to those directions. He thereby brought notions of electrical and magnetic attractions and repulsions into harmony with ideas of stress and strain.

His reference to centres of attraction, magnetic fluids, and lines of force, was intended to recall the three conceptions of the universe whereby philosophers holding various tenets were seeking, respectively, to account for electrical and magnetic phenomena by mechanical analogies. Models were frequently made by men of science, and were as often discarded, broken like toys in the philosophic nursery. The laws of gravity, bequeathed by Newton, explained the motions of the planets, comets, and seas, but they left vague the behaviour of matter at short range, in cohesion, elasticity, and capillarity; they provided insufficient help to electricians. Moreover, concerning the mechanism and operation by which attractions and repulsions are effected, Newton in his wisdom had framed no hypothesis.

Apart from the formulation of theories of the structure and operation of the universe, the practical applications of physical science, even at the beginning of Faraday's era, demanded that electricity and magnetism should be subjected to measurement; for only thus could equipment be efficiently and safely designed, and only thus could the mighty forces involved be brought under control for useful purposes. The task imposed upon leaders in the realm of theoretical and applied physics and mathematics was consequently two-fold:

(1) To account for the phenomena of electrical and magnetic attractions and repulsions, and generally to explain the propagation of electrical and magnetic effects across space or through substances.

(2) To establish laws whereby electrical and magnetic apparatus, circuits, transmission systems, and phenomena could be subjected to quantitative treatment.

Corresponding to this duality, the work at first was divided more or less between academic and technical investigators—at the one extremity the university professors, at the other the telegraph engineers and electricians. For a few years there was between the "professors" and the "practical men" an element of raillery. Towards the end of the century, however, the support that came from the universities, and the high achievements exemplified by contributions to theory from technical men in factories and commercial laboratories, broke down prejudice, and there was established at last, on the basis of mutual appreciation, the fellowship of natural science workers for which Faraday, on neutral ground, had laboured.

The mode of scientific inquiry adopted by Faraday, his attitude towards mathematical analysis, and the predominant position of the mathematicians in his day, might easily have resulted in imperfect or in delayed recognition of his views. Yet it must always be recorded that Faraday was upheld in the camp of the mathematicians themselves, by a champion of his own calibre, who proclaimed him not only a skilled experimenter, but a theorist of most profound and accurate discernment. On December 10, 1855, James Clerk Maxwell read before the Cambridge Philosophical Society a paper on "Faraday's Lines of Force," and in the *Philosophical Magazine*, Vol. XXI, he extended it, pointing out that electrical theory must show the connection between electricity at rest and current electricity, and between the attractions and inductive effects of electricity in both states. Such a

JAMES CLERK MAXWELL.
Born June 13th, 1831.   Died November 5th, 1879.

theory must satisfy laws the mathematical form of which is known, and after simplification it must be capable of expression either as a purely mathematical formula or as a physical hypothesis. He declared that the advantage of the processes of reasoning to be found in the researches of Faraday is that it allows the investigator at each step "to lay hold of a clear physical conception," and he advised his contemporaries to be "neither drawn aside from the subject in pursuit of analytical subtleties nor carried beyond the truth by a favourite hypothesis." This appreciation by Maxwell is the more remarkable because, as he confessed, it related to the physical theory of a science in which, up to that time, he had himself "hardly made a single experiment." Across territory almost unexplored, deep called to deep, and found response.

The immediate object sought by Maxwell was by analysis to place in the hands of "experimental philosophers" the means to interpret their results with precision, in accordance with the principles laid down by Faraday, particularly in respect to lines of force and to the properties of dielectrics. The final result obtained by Maxwell was to weld the whole together and to find his proof in the velocity of light.

To span the gap between qualitative observation and quantitative knowledge has been one of the achievements of the century. To bring electricity and magnetism within the range of measurement, investigators found it necessary first to lay hold of the observed phenomena of attraction and repulsion and to ascertain, by direct weighing or otherwise, the forces exerted between electric charges, in terms of Newtonian length, mass, and time. The next step was to express the results by convention in corresponding terms of the centimetre, the gramme, and the second, which were adopted by the International Congress of Electricians in 1881, as fundamental units—*i.e.* in the "C.G.S." system —universally understood by men of science. By accepting Faraday's notion of lines of force, and his laws of electrolysis, it became possible to construct a bridge between observation and measurement, clear of the troubled waters of speculation. Across this bridge have moved the unconquerable armies of research.

The conception of unit quantity of electricity required, in this process, the application of Coulomb's law, that the force between two quantities of electricity is proportional to the product of those quantities, and is inversely proportional to the square of the distance between them. In the simplest case, the two charges were imagined to be concentrated, respectively, at points—*e.g.* upon conductors of negligible magnitude—so that the force to be expressed numerically was now that between two point-charges, the distance between which could be measured. Unit quantity of electricity was then defined as the charge at each of the two points when there was unit force for unit distance. In like manner, unit quantity of magnetism was defined.

For numerical results, unit electric quantity—*i.e.* unit electric charge—had next to be associated with a definite number of lines of force. Accordingly, the point-charge, corresponding to unit quantity of electricity, was assumed to be at the centre of an imaginary sphere of unit radius. The surface of this sphere was supposed to be marked out into unit squares, and each square was threaded through by a single line of force, radiating straight from the central point charge. As the area of a sphere is 4π times the square of the radius, the sphere of unit radius has an area 4π. By this mode of reasoning, unit quantity of electricity, in air, was assigned 4π lines of electro-static force. Similarly, unit quantity of magnetism—*i.e.* unit magnetic pole—was assigned 4π lines of magnetic force. And, generally, the number thus obtained corresponding to any given quantity of electricity or magnetism, was called "the number of Maxwell lines." Some electricians preferred to regard the quantity itself as the direct measure of the number of lines of force, they omitted the multiplication of the number representing the quantity by 4π, and they obtained what were known as "the number of Faraday lines."

Again, there were physicists who preferred to think of tubes—cylindrical or conical—rather than of lines. The number of tubes is the same as the number of lines. If they are thought of as being square in section, and gradually increasing in area of cross-section as they proceed radially from the point-charge, they can be imagined to fill all space. Space filled with lines or tubes of force constitutes a "field of force," and the number traversing unit area, normally, is the "flux."

When the idea of a field of force was in this manner established, it was found that all the results of Oersted, Ampère, Faraday, and Arago, concerning mechanical movements of electrical or magnetic bodies were brought into harmony; for all the movements are such that (1) A circuit carrying a current endeavours to move to where it will be linked with the greatest number of magnetic lines, *i.e.* to where it will be in the strongest field. (2) A body, which may be a conductor or a dielectric, endeavours to move into the part of the field that will produce the greatest electro-static flux through or at the surface of the body.

The great work accomplished by Faraday in defining and measuring electro-static capacity, was selected as a means of doing honour to his name in the establishment of the unit of electrical capacity— the international farad. The farad is the capacity of a condenser charged to a potential of one international volt by one international coulomb. The international coulomb is the quantity of electricity transferred by a current of one international ampere in one second. The ampere in its practical form rests upon Faraday's law of electrolysis, for it is represented by the steady current that deposits, from a solution of silver-nitrate, metallic silver at the rate of 0.001118 of a gramme in a second. The farad thus defined is too large a unit for most purposes. Consequently the microfarad—which is one-millionth of a farad—is adopted.

The practical need for definitions and precision was exemplified in many ways, but notably in projects to construct submarine cables. At a meeting of the Institution of Civil Engineers on January 13, 1857, it was emphasized that it was Faraday who demonstrated "the excellent non-conducting qualities of gutta-percha, and its fitness for insulating telegraph wires," and that this demonstration furnished the means of realizing the scheme for a Dover-Calais cable "at the exact period when such a discovery was required." The discussion elicited from Faraday an explanation that electrostatic capacity would exert a retarding effect upon telegraphic signals, and that the effect would be greater with submarine cables, because of their higher electrostatic capacity, than with land lines of the same length. His earlier remarks upon gutta-percha, dated February 9, 1848, are to be found in the *Philosophical Magazine* for March, 1848, and in his *Experimental Researches*, Vol. III, p. 494, where he advocates its use "in the arrangement of extemporary or permanent electrical apparatus for the advantage of working philosophers, both juvenile and adult."

While attributing to Faraday his share in the introduction of gutta-percha for electrical purposes, it must be remembered that this material, which has rendered essential service to submarine telegraphy and telephony, was known and was applied to other purposes considerably before 1848. Indeed, Faraday himself had been familiar with it in various forms; for example he says (February, 1848) "it is hardly possible to take one of the soles sold by the shoemakers out of paper, or into the hand, without exciting it to such a degree as to open the leaves of an electrometer one or more inches. . . . Some of the gutta-percha is sold in very thin sheets, resembling in general appearance oiled skin." He does not there explicitly state that it could be used as a dielectric for cables. From the Cantor Lectures of Eugene Obach, in 1897, it appears that the material was brought to Europe by the Tradescants in the seventeenth century. The gum was the subject of discussion at the Society of Arts in 1843, and in that year it attracted special attention on account of demonstrations of its plastic and other mechanical properties, by Dr. José D'Almeida and Dr. Montgomery, both of Singapore. Referring to this occasion, Thomas Hancock, in his treatise published in 1856, remarks that in November, 1843, when Dr. Montgomery "introduced this substance . . . several manufacturers and other persons were furnished with samples and an account of his mode of treating it." A patent dated November 19, 1846, to William Brockedon and Thomas Hancock contains a remarkable list of articles and methods of utilization of gutta-percha. According to Obach, the application of gutta-percha for the insulation of telegraph wires is due to Werner von Siemens, to whom his brother had sent a specimen after receiving it from the Society of Arts. In March, 1848, Werner von Siemens submerged in the Bay of Kiel several miles of copper wire coated with gutta-percha. Faraday expressed his interest in the account of these experiments, in so far as they related to "voltaic induction, and also [to] magnetic induction."

The importance of Faraday's quantitative investigations to the development of theory was manifested by their bearing upon hypotheses concerning the mode of action of forces, whether of attraction or repulsion, throughout the universe. Philosophy had failed to ascertain whether the cause of the tendency of bodies to approach one another is "by spirits emitted," or by "the action of ether or air or of any medium whatsoever, whether corporeal or incorporeal." The first step towards enlightenment was the study of the substance or void between portions of matter, and hence the distinction between conductors and dielectrics. Henry Cavendish, in 1772, had found that, for a given difference of potential, electrical condensers having glass as the dielectric acquire greater charges of electricity than do similar condensers with air as the dielectric, and he obtained numerical data representing this difference of charge. Franklin, in 1755, had supposed that—"the electric fluid" was able to penetrate to a certain depth into glass. Maxwell, in Note 15 of his treatise on the researches of Cavendish, observes that Faraday rediscovered the properties of dielectrics, and that Mossotti "by taking Poisson's memoir and substituting electrical terms for magnetic, and Italian for French," and noticing the analogy between electric and magnetic substances, constructed a mathematical theory of dielectrics. Faraday's extended labours upon specific inductive capacity—described particularly in the Eleventh Series of his Researches—in the year 1837, were intended to determine "whether different dielectric bodies actually do possess any influence over the degree of induction which takes place through them." His view was that, if any such difference exists, it constitutes " an additional and very powerful argument . . . that the whole depends upon a molecular action, in contradistinction to one at sensible distances." The gain to theory and practice was that by accepting Faraday's principles, Maxwell, Kelvin, Hertz, and Heaviside were able to develop consistent equations that fulfilled the requirements of the electromagnetic age.

In his constant effort to free his language from ambiguity Faraday developed remarkable ono-mastic power. His designations entered into the literature and parlance of the electricians of the world. With but few exceptions, his terms are neat and free from objection. "Specific inductive capacity," somewhat clumsy, was occasionally shortened by him to "specific capacity" or even to "capacity"; to-day it has the merit of ensuring discrimination where there are three dielectric "constants"—specific dielectric resistance, specific inductive capacity, and leakance. The term "in-duction" as used by him has suffered change, and deserves special notice. In his vocabulary it is not a mere vector or a coefficient, but in electrical pheno-mena an action excelling in importance all others, for it "has in reality the character of a first, essential, and fundamental principle" governing the har-mony of "electrical excitement by friction, by chemical means, by heat, by magnetic influence, by evaporation, and even by the living being (probably referring to the gymnotus)." Here is perceived his intimacy with the structure and forces of nature. He was impressed with the necessity of admitting: (1) The existence of two forms or directions of forces or electricities, *i.e.* positive and negative; (2) the impossibility of separating them entirely from each other, either in static or in current pheno-mena; (3) the impossibility of charging matter of any kind with one or the other electricity in the complete absence of the other. These conditions urged him to search for "the way in which electrical powers and the particles of matter are related; especi-ally in inductive actions, upon which almost all others appeared to rest."

His attitude towards matter, and his intimacy therewith, is further revealed in his remarks, in the year 1831, concerning the electro-tonic state. At that time he was inclined to the belief that matter, under the influence of "volta-electric or magneto-electric" induction, acquires a peculiar state, "for it resists the formation of an electric current in it, whereas, if in its common condition, such a current would be produced." He describes it as an electrical condition of matter. The suggestion that the state of matter could thus be changed was highly original, but in 1832 he rejected it in favour of "the law under which the induced electric current excited in bodies moving relatively to magnets, is made dependent on the intersection of the magnetic curves by the metal."

The mystery disappears when the fact is recalled that he was experimenting with a closed conducting circuit in a magnetic field. So long as the circuit was fixed and the magnetic field was unchanged in magnitude or direction there was no current in/duced in the circuit. The circuit was then in what he described as the "electro/tonic" state. But with any change of field, lines of force were intersected, and there was a current. This explains, but does not explain away, the electro/tonic state—there may be such a condition of latent action, after all, ready to assist in the production of current when the steady state is being disturbed.

Throughout the era associated with Faraday, in/numerable investigators built up the system of electrical and magnetic measurement applicable to conductors and dielectrics. He gave encourage/ment to the initiation of these activities, but his greatness as an observer and experimenter diverted attention from his work as a measurer. The era began with devices for obtaining quantitative re/sults appertaining to static electric charges. This was followed by a period in which, with few ex/

ceptions, electricians dealt with voltaic currents—ultimately known as "direct" currents. The exceptions arose in cases where short impulses, or transients, as in certain telegraph signals, replaced steady currents. Finally came the period of exceptional difficulty when alternating currents were utilised and subjected to measurement. Magnetic measurements received, early, considerable attention in relation to the earth's field, and in applications to navigation.

Until about the year 1885 there were but few electricians trained to carry out electrical tests beyond simple applications of Ohm's law. Such tests were usually limited to direct-current measurements of the resistance of the conductor, the capacity, and the dielectric resistance. With the extension of land lines and submarine cables, for communication purposes to great distances, however, the aspect of electrical measurement was completely changed. As Faraday had predicted, the effect of distributed capacity was to retard the signals in telegraphy. In telephony, until Heaviside—and later, the valve—solved the riddle of transmission, the distributed capacity and resistance threatened to set a barrier that, for great lengths, would be insurmountable.

Notwithstanding the achievements that charac terised the last half of the century, critics of the educational system complained that measurers had replaced philosophic observers of natural pheno mena. Casual labourers in physical science lamented, moreover, that Faraday had swept the fields too clean, and that he had left too few birds to be beaten out of the bushes. Events proved, how ever, that measurement is an essential part of obser vation; for, with but few exceptions, the great observers were precise measurers. If, for example, Hertz had not been a skilled measurer, he would not have discovered the secret of "tuning" an electrical circuit. If Faraday had been equipped with the measuring facilities of to day, he would have left for others to discover less than a feather in a nest.

Measurement in the Faraday era owed the means to advance to what was accomplished by instru ment makers in furnishing equipment. It was, however, due to the mode of application of such equipment that the victory was secured. The most remarkable progress of this kind is well illustrated by the measurements necessary for the design and maintenance of transmission systems for telephony, telegraphy, electric lighting, and electric power.

The retardation of signals arising from the attenua-tion of current impulses through long conductors was in fact a phenomenon that had to be analysed by measurement, and reduced by skill in design and construction. For this purpose, electricians had at last to familiarize themselves with four cardinal quantities—resistance, capacity, inductance, and leakance, each of which varies with the frequency, and occasionally with the strength, of the alter-nating current utilized. So far as resistance and capacity were concerned, electricians were assisted to comprehend the nature of their problem by ex-perience with early submarine cables, and with the telegraphic equation which had been derived by analogy, following Fourier in a heat problem, by William Thomson (Lord Kelvin). To take account of the four quantities simultaneously, and to carry out such a measurement that each of the four quantities could be assigned a value in the final result, required that electricians should familiarize themselves with calculations relating to complex terms. This was accomplished. By routine method the complexity crystallised out, and the measurers won the day. The application of these methods vastly extended the subjects for research and only the measurers were able to comprehend enough to become observers in the new country. They observed accordingly—and discovered valve-amplifiers. They resolved themselves again into measurers and, helped by inventors, they constructed "repeaters," upon the principle of the relay, utilizing valves and net-works. To-day there is in consequence no terrestrial limit to the distance of transmission that is possible through repeatered systems, and Faraday's problem of retardation is solved for all time.

Whether the philosopher henceforth proceeds by experiment or by analysis, he will do well to study the distinction drawn by Faraday between what is "speculative" and what is "real physical truth." This is set forth in his dissertation on the physical character of the lines of magnetic force, published in the *Philosophical Magazine* for June, 1852. He explains the unique position occupied by gravity among forces acting at a distance, he compares this with what can be ascertained by experiment concerning radiation phenomena, electric forces, and magnetic forces. He admits that his doctrine of lines of force is speculative but he adds:

It is not to be supposed for a moment that speculations of this kind are useless, or necessarily hurtful, in natural philosophy. They should ever be held as doubtful, and liable to error or change; but they are wonderful aids in the hands of the experimentalist and mathematician . . . they lead on, by deduction and correction, to the discovery of new phenomena, and so cause an advance in real physical truth, which, unlike the hypothesis that led to it, becomes fundamental knowledge not subject to change. . . . Though I value them highly when cautiously advanced, I consider it as an essential character of a sound mind to hold them in doubt. . . .

CHAPTER IX

CORRESPONDENCE

IN his correspondence can be traced his effort to keep himself informed of the progress of natural science, chiefly that he might avoid doing injustice to others—for there were but few journals, and no adequate international catalogues or abstracts of current scientific literature. To piece the stray letters of this class into a continuous commentary upon his life between the years 1825-1867 is impossible, but by arranging them in two sequences—relating respectively to home and abroad—they help to show how knowledge and friendship nurtured science in his time.

Here, for example, in May, 1825, is Christie, from the Royal Military Academy, Woolwich, inviting Mr. and Mrs. Faraday to visit that establishment "to see the magnetic experiment" and the effects produced on the magnetic needle by the rotation of metals. Christie refers to some earlier experiments of Mr. Herschel on that subject. Letters pass between Faraday and Lardner in October, 1827, in which Lardner offers him the

Professorship of Chemistry of London University (with a lapse of two years) and Faraday declines on account of reluctance to leave the Royal Institution. Faraday speaks of the investigation of glass that he contemplates. Next come (1828-1829) Minutes of the Sub-Committee, consisting of Dollond, Faraday and Herschel, relating to meetings at Mr. Dollond's house in St. Paul's Churchyard. This is a Sub-Committee to the Committee and Council of the Royal Society, and is appointed to conduct experiments on glass for optical uses at the Royal Institution.

On March 23, 1831, Wheatstone writes to Faraday about the interpretation of some experiments by Savart on the vibrations of a plate; and on January 17, 1846, Wheatstone, from 20, Conduit Street, London, communicates with him about the repulsion of bismuth by a magnet having been discovered by Brugman in 1778, and also about conducting liquids floating in insulating liquids of the same specific gravity. Again, on June 4, 1858, from Lower Mall, Hammersmith, Wheatstone writes to him:

About some trials with my telegraphs. I will also bring a dial for experiments with the electric light. It may be as well for you to read the description of my dial tele-

graph as it existed in 1840 published in the 2nd edition of Daniell's Chemical Philosophy, *p. 578.*

Faraday's curiosity is aroused on April 11, 1835, by a note from William Read referring to particles of hard substance found in West India Wood— brilliant and magnetic. Again, on October 25, 1840, W. G. Armstrong writes to him describing "An electrifying machine of a very novel and economical construction"—which became the famous Armstrong machine for generating static electricity by steam.

One of the hidden treasures is a letter dated May 7, 1845, from Bridgewater Foundry, Patricroft, near Manchester, revealing the growth of the desire for quantitative ideas of energy, from James Nasmyth, who writes to Faraday and illustrates his remarks by finely-drawn sketches suggesting the (energy) equivalent size of a loaf of bread and a glass of gin, equivalent lumps of ironstone, coal required for its reduction, lime required for flux, resulting pig iron, coal required to convert it to a bar of wrought iron, and to a resulting piece of wrought iron. The letter also contains an account of the trial of Nasmyth's pile driver.

I set it on the top of a blunt log of wood 14 inches square, 15 feet long, and let in the steam, when off it set

*a-thumping in good earnest and sent the pile 15 feet down
into hard ground with 20 masterly blows at the rate of 65
per minute! Such pile driving the world never saw before
. . . the following down of the incubus sitting on the head
of the devoted pile was laughable in the extreme. . . .*

In May, 1847, Nasmyth was able to report to
Faraday progress—the pile driver had been of great
use on the Nile dam, and also on the Newcastle
railway bridge work. Others were going to Russia
and to the United States. From three to seven
minutes was the time required to drive a pile of
fifty feet thirty-five feet into the ground—against
twenty-four to thirty hours by the old process, "the
whole apparatus sitting upon the shoulders of the
pile and going down with it."

Nasmyth is also concerned with the hardening
of steel, and he wants Faraday to try sending a
current through steel wire during the hardening
process. He scratches sheet glass with coke (in the
sun preferred) at hazard, and directs attention to
the interference colours thus easily obtained. On
June 15, 1848, he writes to Faraday:

*The Emperor of Russia has just sent me a most mag-
nificent diamond ring containing 140 diamonds (which I
don't intend to reduce to coke) in testimony of his high
satisfaction with the performance of two of my pile drivers*

which I sent him for the foundation work of the great arsenal at Cronstadt.

Lastly, on May 21, 1847, Nasmyth writes:

> *. . . in relation to a great mystery, namely the cause of hardening of steel, than which there is not a process of more value to mankind I know of—civilization rests on it alone. What I want to get at is one or two new facts by varying the ordinary process.*
>
> *First experiment, or question I want to ask Nature, is: What is the effect in respect to hardening or otherwise when a bit of steel wire (at usual hardening temperature) is plunged into cold water, while the steel wire in question is at the time part of a pretty powerful galvanic circuit? Has such a state of circumstances any effect on the steel as regards hardening? . . . The experiment . . . might lead to something . . . perhaps important. . . . The hardening of steel is so complete a mystery as yet, as far as I know, that it is by such novel or out of the usual way treatment that we hope to stumble on the end of the thread of some interesting facts.*

On May 30, 1845, George Rennie directed Faraday's attention to Venturi's experiments (1826). Amongst the correspondence also are items appertaining to the development of optics. Thus, in 1849, Warren de la Rue writes to him requesting that he would send to Mr. Nobert of Greifswald, Pomerania—a maker of microscopes and other philosophical instruments—a piece of heavy glass. De la Rue adds:

The applicant has accomplished, at my suggestion, some dividing on glass of such extreme fineness that it is a question whether the physical properties of light do not prevent our resolving it—the divisions being about the one hundred and ten thousandth of an inch apart from centre to centre, and therefore considerably less than the wavelengths of even the violet rays. . . . It is a mechanical wonder, and reflects the highest credit on the patience and skill of Mr. Nobert.

Here also is a communication of importance relating to the work of Stokes at Cambridge.

JAN. 26, 1853.   LOWER MALL, HAMMERSMITH.

MY DEAR FARADAY,

If you will send to King's College, Mr. Miller will let you have the original revolving mirror with the whirling table to which it is fitted. I have spoken to him about it. I have at home a small revolving mirror ($\frac{1}{4}$ of an inch square) with a watch movement making 200 revolutions per second with a tolerably accurate means of measuring the angular elongation of the spark, which I have used to measure the duration of sparks in electro-magnetic coils. Mr. Stokes can also have this if it will be of any service to him.

Yours very truly,

C. WHEATSTONE.

On October 31, 1853, Latimer Clark writes to Faraday from the Engineers' Office of the Electric Telegraph Company, 448 West Strand, with regard to

. . . the return charge quite sensible to the tongue from a coil of 10 yards of gutta-percha wire covered with lead. . . . I am determined to get evidence (if possible) of the disturbance of one wire by another. We ought to see it when circuit is broken despite of imperfect insulation.

With characteristic zeal, Snow Harris—known as "thunder and lightning Harris"—in a letter to Faraday of May 20, 1855, suggests an experiment:

Put some coarse grains of the impure zinc of commerce into a glass bottle A. Pour on them dilute sulphuric acid. The water will decompose and hydrogen will escape at b. If, during effervescence, a gold-leaf electrometer be applied to the glass vessel A, its leaves will diverge freely.

Amongst the loose papers treasured in the Library of the Institution of Electrical Engineers, is the correspondence between Faraday and Prof. G. G. Stokes, towards the end of the year 1855, on the behaviour of small suspended bars of paramagnetic and diamagnetic substances, respectively, in magnetic fields that are uniform or not, respectively. Faraday had examined particularly the case of phosphorus in such fields, and had found a mystery: Why does a diamagnetic bar oppose less obstacle to the passage of the lines of force when it is perpendicular than when it is parallel to them? Stokes writes to Faraday (November 13, 1855):

I asked if the fact was so, and you referred me to the experiment with the phosphorus. But after having maturely considered the thing, I believe the true way of explaining the mystery is by denying the fact. I do not, of course, mean questioning the result obtained with the phosphorus. That was no doubt all right; but the setting of the phosphorus is explicable otherwise, namely from the non-uniformity of the field of force. I think theory may be trusted for the mode of setting of a bar in a perfectly uniform field.

Towards the end of 1857, *i.e.* on November 9, Maxwell writes to Faraday from 129 Union Street, Aberdeen, to acknowledge the receipt of papers on the Relations of Gold to Light, and on the Conservation of Force. Maxwell here defines Energy as the power a thing has of doing work, arising either from its own motion, or from the "tension" subsisting between it and other things. Force he defines as the tendency of a body to pass from one place to another. It depends upon the amount of change of "tension" which that passage would produce. He declares that Faraday is, so far as he knows, the first person in whom the idea of bodies acting at a distance by throwing the surrounding medium into a state of constraint, had arisen, as a principle actually to be believed in. Maxwell continues:

We have had streams of hooks and eyes flying around magnets, and even pictures of them so beset, but nothing is clearer than your descriptions of all sources of force keeping up a state of energy in all that surrounds them, which state by its own increase or diminution measures the work done by any change in the system. You seem to see the lines of force curving round obstacles and driving plump at conductors and swerving towards certain directions in crystals, and carrying with them everywhere the same amount of attractive power spread wider or denser as the lines widen or contract. You have also seen that the great mystery is not how like bodies repel and unlike attract, but how like bodies attract (by gravitation). But if you can get over that difficulty, either by making gravity the residual of the two electricities or by simply admitting it, then your lines of force can "weave a web across the sky" and lead the stars in their courses without any necessarily immediate connection with the objects of their attraction.

The lines of force from the sun spread out from him and when they come near a planet curve out from it, *so that every planet diverts a number depending on its mass from their course and substitutes a system of its own so as to be something like a comet, if* lines of force were visible. . . . *Now conceive every one of these lines (which never interfere but proceed from sun and planet to infinity) to have a pushing force instead of a pulling one, and then sun and planet will be pushed together with a force which comes out as it ought proportional to the product of the masses and the inverse square of the distance.*

The difference between this case and that of the dipolar forces is, that instead of each body catching the lines of force from the rest all the lines keep as clear of other bodies as they can, and go off to the infinite sphere against which I [Maxwell] have supposed them to push.

Here then we have conservation of energy (actual and potential) as every student of dynamics learns, and besides this, we have conservation of "lines of force" as to their number and total strength—for every body always sends out a number proportional to its own mass, and the pushing effect of each is the same. All that is altered when bodies approach is the direction in which these lines push. . . .

In a different mood, on November 30, 1859, Maxwell writes to Faraday from Marischal College, Aberdeen:

DEAR SIR,

I am a candidate for the Chair of Natural Philosophy in the University of Edinburgh, which will soon be vacant by the appointment of Professor J. D. Forbes to St. Andrews. If you should be able, from your knowledge of the attention which I have paid to science, to recommend me to the notice of the Curators, it would be greatly in my favour and I should be much indebted to you for such a certificate.

I was sorry that I had so little time in September that I could not write out an explanation of the figures of lines of force which I sent you, but Professor W. Thomson, to whom I lent them, seems to have indicated all that was necessary, and most of them can be recognised from their resemblance to the curves made with iron filings.

The only thing to be observed is that these curves are due to action either of long wires perpendicular to the paper, or of elongated magnetic poles such as the edge of a long ribbon of steel magnetised transversely. By considering infinitely long currents or magnetic poles perpendicular to the paper, we obtain systems of curves far more easily traced than in any other case, while their general appearance is similar to those produced in the ordinary experiments.

All the diagrams have two sets of lines at right angles to each other, and the width between the two sets of lines is the same, so that the reticulation is nearly square. If one system belongs to poles, the other belongs to currents, so that if the meaning of one be known, that of the other may be deduced from it.

I remain,

Yours truly,

JAMES CLERK MAXWELL.

Professor Faraday.

Also on May 21, 1861, there is a letter from 8 Palace Gardens Terrace, W., from Maxwell, giving a general statement to Faraday of the rotation of a body nearly a sphere—and ending "I have my dynamical top in London, and can show you the motion at any time."

Here may be examined the following letter from William Thomson (Lord Kelvin) to Faraday, dated November 17, 1859, from 2 The College, Glasgow:

MY DEAR SIR,

I have made an experiment to-day which illustrates remarkably the electropolar state which you have always urged must exist in the particles of an electrolyte between two metals having different degrees of affinity for one of its elements; and I cannot deny myself the pleasure of immediately telling you of it.

An uninsulated can of water was placed so as to discharge its contents through a vertical copper pipe and fine nozzle of copper in a stream breaking into drops after about an inch, and falling into an insulated *jar connected with an electrometer. A tube of metal, either zinc, composition (chiefly copper), or common sheet copper, was sometimes held round the stream of water and sometimes it was left simply with air and the walls of the room round it. In the last-mentioned case, the electrometer quickly showed strong negative, because the air of the room and a plate glass electrical machine not far off which had been in use, electrified the* uninsulated *metal tube and issuing stream* negatively *by influence. When a* copper *tube was held round the stream, the electrometer showed little or no effect. When a piece of bent sheet zinc was held in the hand round the stream, and the vertical copper* pipe was touched by the same hand, the electrometer showed nothing or slight positive. When a metal wire connected the sheet zinc round the stream with the copper pipe from which the stream issued, the electrometer very quickly gathers a strong negative charge. In thirty seconds it showed 65° negative.

When a composition metal (nearly copper) tube was used, the electrometer gathered 7° negative in the thirty seconds. When a wide zinc tube, about six inches diameter and twelve inches long was held vertically, so that the stream broke into drops about its centre, the electrometer gathered negative quickly, provided the zinc was connected by metal with the copper from which the water issued. By using a well-insulated support a spark may readily be obtained by allowing the charge to gather. I shall write to you again when I have got one.

That the result must be as I found it, seemed obvious before I made the experiment, from the following considerations:

If the two water-arcs (moist cotton wicks for instance) shown in sketch, are brought together, a current flows in the direction shown by the arrowheads. Hence, before the ends of the water-arcs are united, it must tend to flow, and these opposed ends must be oppositely electrified—that connected with the zinc positively, and that connected with the copper negatively. If drops from the former are allowed to fall through a hole in the zinc, they must each carry away negative electricity by the dynamical power of the gravitation of the water, and communicate it to any conductor into which they may be allowed to fall.

This explains completely Volta's contact and separa~
tion experiment by electro~chemical action, if there be any
moisture present between the plates. For at the instant
when the last point of metallic contact still exists, the
moist film on the copper surface must be negative to the
moist film on the zinc surface; and the thinness of the
separating air must make the quantity large even for a small
difference of potentials between the opposed water surfaces.

Immediately, and even after contact (the insulation of
glass handles being perfect) each metal has and keeps the
electricity its (assumed moist) surface had when opposed
to the other, and thus the copper shows negative and the
zinc positive after separation.

It would be important to try Volta's experiments in
artificially dried atmospheres of various gases.

The experiment which I made to~day was done by the
aid of my divided ring electrometer. Perhaps one cell
Daniell would, as the electrometer stood in the experi~
ment, have given about $2°$. The effects I observed are
capable of indefinite accumulation and to the extent I had
them, would, I believe, have shown on a gold~leaf electro~
meter.   Believe me,
                  Yours most truly,
                        WILLIAM THOMSON.

P.S. I think I must ask that, if wanted to lecture on
atmospheric electricity, I should have some time later than
the 7th of May, as I fear I should have no time for pre~
paration sufficient before the 1st of the month.

Professor Faraday.

On April 26, 1860, Henry E. Roscoe, from Owens College, Manchester, wrote to Faraday to tell him that Bunsen had discovered a new alkaline metal by "special analysis, *i.e.* the identification of the constitutents of a body by means of the various colours which these constituents impart to a flame."

To convey now a hint of the character and extent of Faraday's foreign correspondence, it is well to begin by observing that, in January, 1822, Ampère, from Paris, writes to Faraday describing his experiments upon moving conductors.

Ampère complains of

Un savant italien (who has raised doubts) non sur ma théorie, mais sur des conséquences que j'en avais déduites et qu'il ne croyait pas fondées . . . sur des raisonnements spécieux, mais dénués de fondement.

Eleven years later, on a different subject, there is a letter from Faraday to Ampère, May 4, 1833:

I am extremely indebted to you for your kindness in putting me right.

On August 27, 1834, Amedeo Avogadro, from Turin, sent to Faraday "avec la plus parfaite considération" a copy of his memoir on the specific heat of solids and liquids.

Next is to be found a somewhat blunt description, dated 15th November, 1833, from Utrecht, by Mohl, addressed to Faraday, of impressions of a visit to "the celebrated university of Göttingen," with an account of the telegraph of the immortal Gauss. Mohl says:

. . . No one doubts but that Gauss is a man of genius, perhaps the first mathematician living, still he is not a good lecturer, and so far useless, and his observatory . . . looks much as if little use was made of it. . . . Stromeyer has certainly a neat laboratory, but nothing like what may be seen in twenty places in England, besides that, in my opinion, there is a great want of apparatus . . . and if I am not mistaken, the lectures of old Blumenbach would scarcely draw an audience to the lecture room of a Mechanics' Institution. Their library, however, it must be said, is excellent, and challenges, as far as usefulness is concerned, any other in existence.

Gauss has got up a very neat apparatus, a sort of magnetic telegraph. Two bar magnets of a pound weight, and suspended in different places in a distance of about $1\frac{1}{2}$ miles (English), each has wires coiled round but not touching them, these wires communicate, through the open air over roofs and steeples and the action of a couple of galvanic plates in one place gives motion to the magnet placed at the distance of $1\frac{1}{2}$ miles. The thing at any rate is very curious. . . . I have read with great pleasure your new series of experiments. They are sure to carry your name down to posterity as long as there will be anything existing like science.

Here also is the letter of Matteucci of Florence to Faraday, March 12, 1836, and Faraday's reply upon the question of priority for the law (in Faraday's words) that the chemical power of *a current of electricity is in direct proportion to the quantity of electricity which passes*, which Faraday had enunciated in December, 1832.

Dr. Peyrou, Professor of Natural Philosophy, of Marseilles, writes to him from Paris, 20th August, 1841, mentioning that he has undertaken

. . . *the translation of your Experimental Researches— the very code of electricians—of which I am ambitious to endow my own country.*

Faraday writes to Becquerel from the Royal Institution, December 30, 1850.

. . . *I developed and* published *the nature and principles of the action of magnetic and diamagnetic media upon substances in them more or less magnetic or diamagnetic than themselves, in the year 1845, or just* five *years ago. The paper was read by the Royal Society, 8th January, 1846, and is contained in the* Philosophical Transactions *for 1846, p. 50 etc. If you refer to the numbered paragraphs 2357, 2363, 2367, 2400k, 2406, 2414, 2423, 2438, you will see at once how far I had gone at that date. The papers were re-published in* Poggendorf's Annalen, *and I believe in the Geneva and Italian and German Journals in one form or another.*

In reference to the magnetism of oxygen, three years ago, i.e. in 1847, I showed its high magnetic character in relation to nitrogen and all other gases, and that air owed its place amongst them to the oxygen it contained. I even endeavoured to analyse the air, separating its oxygen and nitrogen by magnetic force, for I thought such a result possible. All this you will find in a paper published in the Philosophical Magazine *for 1847, Vol. XXXI, page 401 etc. The paper was also published at full length in* Poggendorf's Annalen, *1848, Vol. LXIII, page 256 etc. . . . In it you will find the effect of heat on oxygen, air, etc. The experiments were all revised, and made upon the principles before developed concerning the mutual relation of substances and the media surrounding them. This year (1850) I have been busy extending the above researches and have sent in several papers to the Royal Society, and have also given a Bakerian Lecture in which they were briefly summed up.*

Concerning these effects, he referred to the later experiments of Mr. E. Becquerel, who made "excellent measurements which I had not." Reference may also be made to the *Philosophical Magazine* of December, 1847, for Faraday's paper "On the Diamagnetic Conditions of Flame and Gases."

In 1848, Plücker, who at first corresponded with Faraday in French, visited England and became closely acquainted with him. Thereafter he wrote in English. On his return to Bonn, he says:

Struck by one of your observations, the first thing I did was to direct my attention to the experiments respecting the different laws of intensity for magnetism and diamagnetism.

The results obtained by Faraday and Plücker in this research were compared, but did not always agree. The differences were attributed to the presence probably of iron in some of the crystals. On December 4, 1849, Plücker writes to Faraday:

Some weeks ago, in repeating Boutigny's experiments, I put my hand into melted iron at 1500° C. without feeling within any heat whatever. It is curious.

And again, in February, 1853, from Bonn:

Mr. Geissler, our clever artist, constructed a year ago, for the use of wine-makers, an apparatus indicating the quantity of alcohol, by the tension of the vapours of the mixture mixed with a certain quantity of air, all at the temperature of 100° C.

Faraday sent Plücker a specimen of heavy glass which caused him to carry out a series of most fruitful experiments.

Plücker renewed the correspondence in 1857, and included an account of the Bonn experiments with rarefied gases, magnetic and diamagnetic induction, and magneto crystallic actions. On August 17 of that year he invited him to Bonn to the thirty-third meeting of the German Association:

You don't like festivals, I know, but you may here move quite free. You don't like travelling abroad, but changing the air of London and its environs with the air of the Rhine, will certainly do good to your health. When my own head is tired, I run away in any direction, and when returned I feel myself restored.

> *With all my heart,*
> *Yours,*
> *PLÜCKER.*

In 1852, Faraday was in communication with Plateau of Gand, and with Peltier; and in 1854 he had an extended correspondence with Macedoine Melloni of Naples on electrostatic induction and other matters.

A further link with Germany is to be found in the correspondence with Knochenhauer of Meiningen in 1856, although Knochenhauer wrote to Faraday in French. This discussion related chiefly to specific inductive capacity, and to the method of measuring it (*Annales de Pogg*, XCIII, p. 407, 1854). It may be recalled that it was with Knochenhauer spirals that Hertz subsequently began his epoch-making investigations upon electro-magnetic waves at Karlsruhe.

The esteem in which Faraday was held throughout Europe is well exemplified by the following letter to him from Hansteen:

OBSERVATORY, CHRISTIANA, 30 DEC., 1857.
DEAR AND HONOURED SIR,

I thank you heartily for your letter of 16 December, at first while you have written yourself, as you could better declare the circumstances, and secondly, while I thereby have received an autographic letter from a man which I in many years have honoured as one of the chief notabilities "in rebus magneticis." I preserve with delight and perhaps a little vanity letters from different English scientifical notabilities, as Sir Joseph Banks, Sir David Brewster, Professor Airy, Professor Forbes, General Sabine, Professor Barlow, and others; and to this treasure I now can add yours.

Professor Oersted was a man of genius, but he was a very unhappy experimenter; he would not manipulate instruments. He must always have an assistant or one of his auditors, who had easy hands to arrange the experiment; I have often in this way assisted him as his auditor. Already in the former century there was a general thought, that there was a great conformity and perhaps identity betweeen the electrical and magnetical force; it was only the question how to demonstrate it by experiments. Oersted had tried to place the wire of his galvanic battery perpendicular (at right angles) over the magnetical needle, but remarked no sensible motion. Once, after the end of his lecture as he had used a strong galvanic battery to other experiments, he said "let us now once, as the battery is in activity, try to place the wire parallel with the needle." As this was made he was quite struck with perplexity by seeing the needle making a great oscillation (almost at right angles with the magnetic meridian). Then he said: "let us now invert the direction of the current," and the needle deviated in the contrary direction. Thus the great detection was made; and it has been said, not without reason, that he tumbled over it by accident. He had not before any more idea than any other person that the force should be transversal. *But as Lagrange said of Newton in a similar occasion, "Such accidents only meet persons who deserve them."*

You completed the detection by inverting the experiment, by demonstrating that an electrical current *can be excited by a* magnet; *and this was no accident, but a consequence of a clear idea. I pretermit your many later important detections, which will conserve your name with golden letters in the history of magnetism.*

Gauss was the first, who applied your detection to give telegraphic signals from the Observatory in Göttingen to the Physical Hall in a distance of almost an English mile from the Observatory.

I very well understand your situation. I can also not work in company with other persons, and I read not much, for not to be distracted from my own way of thinking. I allow that thereby many things escape me, but I fear to be distracted on sideways. "Non omnia possumus omnes." Everyone must follow his own nature.

I have translated an extract of your letter, and sent it to Göttingen to Mr. Andsten.

In the summer of 1819, I visited in long time almost every day the library in "Royal Institution" in order to extract magnetical observations (declination and inclination) from old works, which our University was not in possession of, for instance Hackluyt and Purchas his pilligrims, etc. So I am acquainted with the place of your activity.

I have this year received your portrait from Lenoir in Vienna, and also of Sir David Brewster. They shall decorate my study on the side of Oersted, Bessel, Gauss and Struve.

> *Believe me, Sir,*
> *Sincerely your*
> *Very respectful*
> *CHR. HANSTEEN.*

On January 21, 1858, Antoine d'Abbadie writes to Faraday for details of composition and manufacture of the heavy glass. In 1858 Faraday receives also a letter from his friend De La Rive, from Geneva, who had heard that Faraday was occupying himself with the luminous and remarkable effects produced by the electric discharges of the Rhumkorff apparatus in Geissler tubes, and the influence that magnetism has on the discharges. He mentions that Plücker was working at the same subject at Bonn.

Joseph Henry writes to him on November 3, 1866, from the Smithsonian Institution, Washington, asking "What is actually doing by the Lighthouse Authorities of England in the way of experiment with the electrical light, and particularly with that derived from Wild's apparatus?" In January and April of 1866, Faraday received letters from H. Wilde, from Manchester, describing the Wilde dynamo.

On May 28, 1855, John Gassiot in a letter to Faraday referred to a paper (*R. S. Trans.* 1844), concerning the state of an electrolyte before actual electrolysis takes place, observing that "this is similar to the induced state of an electrified body previous to its receiving the actual discharge from the machine."

CHAPTER X

PUBLIC SERVICES

OFFICIAL letters also crowded in from all quarters to Faraday. Towards the close of the more active part of his career he gave up all professional occupation, he pursued his own researches, but, as he expressed it, he always held himself ready to assist the Government "if still in my power, *not for pay*." He added "I have the honour and pleasure of applications . . . from the Admiralty, the Ordnance, the Home Office, the Woods and Forests, and other departments, all of which I have replied to, and will reply to as long as strength is left me." (*Vide* a letter to Lord Auckland, quoted by Dr. J. H. Gladstone.) Letters from Prince Louis Napoleon are included in Volume II of *Faraday's Life and Letters*, by Bence Jones. In January, 1839, Faraday was in correspondence with the military authorities at Chatham, who consulted him concerning the electrical arrangements for detonating gunpowder. It appears that the method of insulating the "leading wires" at that time was to enclose them in tape "sewed round and covered with waterproof composition—a mixture of pitch, bees-wax and tallow." Two such leading wires were then "attached to contrary sides of a rope, and bound round with small cord and served with yarns." In the same year (1839) the question of how to test "battery power" was referred by the Chatham establishment to Faraday. The object of these investigations was to find the best means of blowing up the wreck of the *Royal George*.

In 1845, he was again in touch with the military authorities, for Mr. G. W. Hearn, of the Royal Military College, Sandhurst, sent him the results of a mathematical study of "the mutual action of voltaic circuits." On August 26, 1847, he received a letter from the Admiralty:

SIR,

I am commanded by my Lords Commissioners of the Admiralty to request that you will, in conjunction with Lieut.-Colonel Irvine, the Director of Engineering and Architectural Works at Somerset House, report upon the working of Mr. Gamble's Electro Magnetic Telegraph upon the Great Western Railway.

I have the honor (sic) to be,
Sir,
Your most obedient Servant,
W. A. B. HAMILTON.

He replied, on August 30, 1847, to Captain Hamilton, Secretary of the Admiralty, that owing to ill-health and to other reasons, he was unable to accede to the request. The "other reasons" were slight resentment that he had not received a reply to a former report.

He was asked, on March 3, 1852, by the Office of Ordnance to advise on the analysis of the explosive contents of a French shell after the attack on Salee. As he reported on this on March 5, 1852, giving the analysis, he must be given credit for having been a quick chemist.

On April 7, 1853, Inglefield, who was about to explore in Arctic regions, wrote to him from H.M.S. *Phoenix*, at Woolwich, informing him that he (Inglefield) had been appointed to the command, and suggesting that he would like an interview some morning to discuss "magnetical or electrical research" in those high latitudes. He added: "Mr. Gassiot informs me about nine is generally the most agreeable hour to you."

To illustrate the diversity of subjects that he investigated, from his youth upwards, and upon which he was consulted, it suffices to refer to a few of his memoranda. Here is a note dated February 10, 1820:

Went to-day to Mr. Perkins to see his apparatus and specimens for the transference of engravings from plate to plate. He takes blocks of steel, softens them by some process of decarbonisation, so that a knife cuts them almost in the manner of lead. Exquisite engravings are then made on them by the hand and by lathes. The blocks are then re-carbonised and converted into hard steel, and this in such an admirable way that the engraving suffers not the slightest injury. . . . Mr. Perkins showed us an instrument he had made to [demonstrate] the compressibility of water. . . . Mr. Perkins had also a sounding machine.

On November 5, 1838, De La Beche, Director of the Museum of Economic Geology, consults Faraday concerning the building stone to be used in the construction of the new Parliament Houses. De La Beche reminds him that:

While certain kinds of magnesian limestone are extremely durable, others decompose very readily, e.g. York Minster (in a wretched state), and Southwell (in nearly as good condition as when erected by the Normans). Similarly for sandstones, and Portland stone, country and London, frost, moisture.

De La Beche refers to "having spoken also to Wheatstone at the Athenaeum about it."

On April 16, 1846, R. Sheepshanks consulted him about the preservation of a standard yard which he had been commissioned to make, and on

July 1, 1856, Faraday is requested by the Trustees of the British Museum

To advise their architect, Mr. Smirke, in choosing the best substratum on which to lay the gold which is to be applied to the ribs, mouldings, and other parts of the dome over the new Reading Room, also the quality of gold-leaf, and thickness of metal, so that the gilding might be finished in a superior and lasting manner.

Whatever he advised in this respect was successful, for the gilding remained in excellent condition. In 1861 he advised the Trustees concerning efflorescence that appeared upon some of the vases in the Museum. Here also is a letter dated March 22, 1865, from the "Council on Education, Kensington Museum":

Have you any recollection of stating to any Committee or Commission your opinion that if Raphael's Cartoons were removed to the National Gallery in Trafalgar Square, they would be damaged there? . . .

Faraday is sometimes himself the inquirer. In the next letter the British Museum authorities, for instance, are appealed to for a specimen for a lecture.

ROYAL INSTITUTION,
13th MARCH, 1845.

MY DEAR SIR,

After Easter I must lecture upon Gold, and am very anxious, if possible, to show my audience some very

ancient specimens of the metal. Now I suppose you have some of the most ancient in the form of gilt mummy. I have thought that perhaps you might feel at liberty to lend me a specimen at the time, of which I will take the very greatest care, but if I am inadvertently thinking a very improper thing I hope you will forgive me.

Ever yours faithfully,

M. FARADAY.

J.W. Pettigrew, Esq.

From an earlier letter, it appears that somebody suggested that at a Friday meeting of the Royal Institution a mummy should be opened. Faraday in fact wrote to J. W. Pettigrew also on May 4, 1835, for the loan of some gilt articles from a mummy for a Saturday afternoon lecture at the Royal Institution.

A specimen of the kind of correspondence that caused the laboratory to resound with Faraday's laughter may here be reproduced:

DEPARTMENT OF THE SURVEYOR OF Yᵉ NAVY
WHITEHALL,
APRIL 26, 1835.

SIR,

With reference to the experiments made by you and Sir Humphry Davy in 1823-24 on the preservation of copper sheathing, I wish to take the liberty of troubling you with a question.

The iron and zinc protectors seem to have failed

from two causes. First—the conversion of the protecting metals into oxides, and the destruction of their influence appears to have taken place before the vessel could be docked to have the worn ones replaced; and secondly—the rusty surfaces of the protectors were nuclei for the deposition of earthy particles and the formation of a bed for seaweed and shell-fish.

It has struck me that both these evils could be avoided if the protectors were placed in a water-tight cistern inside the ship, at about the height of the water-line—so that a communication could be kept up between the inside of the box, and the sea-water without by means of a tube.

> Your obedient servant,
> NATH¹· BARNABY.

Reply by Faraday:

SIR,

The proposition is of no value. The protector would preserve the inside of the box, but would be utterly useless as regards the ship's sheathing.

> I am,
> Your obedient servant,
> M. FARADAY.

It is fitting to conclude this brief review of the correspondence by directing attention to two letters relating to the death of Faraday's faithful friend and assistant Sergeant Anderson. They require no comment:

On January 12, 1866, Sir James South writes

SERGEANT ANDERSON AT WORK IN FARADAY'S LABORATORY
AT THE ROYAL INSTITUTION (1852).

From a painting by Miss Harriet Moore. Presented to the Royal Institution by
Miss Julia Moore, February 2nd, 1885.

to Faraday from the Observatory at Kensington about the death of Anderson:

About 22 years' exemplary service as a soldier and 37 or 38 years' service as Chemical Assistant to Mr. Faraday in his immortal experiments in the Laboratory of the Royal Institution, I would take upon myself the charge of purchasing a site in the Cemetery at Highgate or elsewhere rather than suffer the mortal remains of our humble friend to lie promiscuously with ordinary dead.

In a letter from the Royal Society, February 3, 1865, Faraday gives some particulars concerning this grand old warrior:

[Anderson] came to assist in the glass-house for the service of science in September, 1827, where he remained working until about 1830. Then for a while he was retained by myself until in 1832 he was in the service of the Royal Institution, and paid by it. From that time to the present he has remained with that body, and has obtained their constant approbation. In January, 1842, they raised his pay to £100 per annum, with praise. In 1847 they raised it in like manner to £110. For the same reason they, in 1853, raised it to £120, and in 1860 . . . in consideration of his now lengthened service and the diligence exhibited by him . . . to £130, to be paid out of the Laboratory Fund in like manner as his existing salary. Mr. Anderson still remains with us, and is in character what he ever has been. He and I are companions in years, in work, and in the Royal Institution. Mr. Anderson

was 75 years of age on 12th of last month. He is a widower, but has a daughter keeping his house for him. We wish him not to come to the Royal Institution save when he is well enough to make it a pleasure, but he seems to be happy being so employed.

CHAPTER XI

COMMONPLACE BOOKS

THE imperfect state of co-ordination of scientific and general knowledge in his day led Faraday to collect information in note-books. To one of these he gives the title, "Chemical Notes, Hints, Suggestions, and Objects of Pursuit," and in it there is his comment:

I already owe much to these notes, and think such a collection worth the making by every scientific man. I am sure none would think the trouble lost after a year's experience.

M. F., 1822.

It is instructive to observe that amongst these "Chemical Notes" he has the classification: "Nitrogen, Sulphur, Phosphorus, Carbon, Oxygen, Iodine, Fluorine, Electricity, Heat and Light, Organic Chemistry, Metals, Immediate." Thus, while his mind was at work upon subjects for his lectures, it was alert upon matters calling for immediate investigation in the laboratory. The immediate matters were items resulting from direct observation:

The use of sub-borate of lead as blowpipe flux, conden-

sation of carbonic oxide, prevention of tarnish of gold-leaf and silver, crystallisation of cod's-head bones, shadows of thumb from several windows, crystallised Prussian blue.

Here, for example, with regard to silver, is a note of his: "Cut silver tarnishes rapidly, rubbed silver does not."

The earlier notes are of endless variety, from serious to grotesque. To account for the diversity, it must be remembered that in the process of self-education to which he subjected himself, he was not wholly absorbed in chemistry and physics. Elocution, drawing, literature, theology, music, social life, fun and fellowship, make up the tale—yet wherever he set his hand, heart, or mind, his desire for knowledge was insatiable.

How early he acquired the desire to accumulate information is illustrated in a manuscript book now in the possession of the Institution of Electrical Engineers. It is called by him *The Philosophical Miscellany*, and it is dated 1809-1810. He describes it as

A collection of Notices, Occurrences, Events, etc., relating to the Arts and Sciences, collected from the Public Papers, Reviews, Magazines, and other miscellaneous works. Intended to promote both Amusement and Instruction and also to corroborate [sic] or invalidate those

theories which are continually starting in the world of science.

Its chief value is to indicate his avidity for all statements bearing upon direct observation of natural phenomena. It contains some of his careful sketches, and it is provided with an index, written in his own hand. Among the subjects are: Fire-eating, properties of camphor, candle screens, coloured flames, detonation, electric fish, fairy rings, the invisible girl, the effect of garlic on moles, glow worms, incombustible wood, lightning, rust, how to loosen glass stopples, and the alleged curing of toothache by magnetism.

This treasure belonged to Miss Jane Barnard, by whom it was given to Mr. W. M. Mordey, who presented it to the Library of the Institution of Electrical Engineers, on November 18, 1915.

On February 22, 1833, Faraday appeared for the first time as Fullerian Professor of Chemistry, at the Royal Institution. He chose as the subject of his discourse "The Practical Prevention of Dry Rot in Timber." The method advocated by him was, as he pointed out, the invention of J. Howard Kyan, and it consisted in treating the timber with corrosive sublimate. The pamphlet containing the account of this lecture is now very scarce—there is no copy either in the British Museum, the Royal Society, the Royal Institution, or the Athenaeum libraries. Two copies, are, however, to be found in the Library of the Institution of Electrical Engineers. According to the statements made by Faraday on this occasion, the need for such a method of wood-preservation was particularly pressing in the Navy, for the amount of timber utilised at that time in the construction of a ship is here recorded to have been:

A first-rate (90 guns or upwards) 5880 loads.
A second-rate (80 guns)   4339 „
A third-rate (70 guns)   3600 „
A fourth-rate   2372 „
A fifth-rate   1800 „
A sixth-rate (28 guns)   963 „

He observes that H.M.S. *Rodney*, launched in 1809, scarcely put to sea when all her fastenings became loose from defective timber, and that H.M.S. *Dublin*, launched in February, 1812, "returned to Plymouth in 1813 in so dreadful a state that she was ordered to be paid off."

Here is a note entered by him in 1817 that speaks for itself:

What precise quantity of misery is thrust into that space of human life which extends from six to sixteen years of age . . . The cries of infant misery extend from one end of Europe to the other.

THE INSTITUTION OF ELECTRICAL ENGINEERS, LONDON, 1930.

He then quotes, as follows, the record of a German schoolmaster who died after fifty-one years of inflicting misery:

"911,500 canings.
121,000 floggings.
209,000 custodes (imprisonments).
136,000 tips with the ruler.
10,200 boxes on the ear.
22,700 tasks by heart.
700 boys to stand on peas.
6,000 kneel on a sharp edge of wood.
5,000 wear the fool's cap.
1,700 hold the rod."

The Commonplace book contains also an extract revealing that Faraday was alive to the traffic problems of his day. It is from the *Liverpool Courier* of September, 1823:

Walking the streets—*It has been found a difficult thing at Liverpool to make the townsfolk adopt the well-known and useful rule of keeping the right-hand side of the path in walking; and reason having failed, an attempt has been made to shame them into obedience to it, the following courteous placard having appeared on the walls of the town:*

"Respectable people *are requested to keep the* right hand side *of the footpath and* Blackguards *the* left."

There is also a remarkable account of his interview on July 1, 1816, with the Calculating Boy. This lad was able mentally to find cube roots of such numbers as 20368783891. Faraday says of him:

Zerah Colburn is about 13 years of age, nothing very striking in his countenance, yet a high forehead and red hair readily distinguish him . . . has learned the French and German languages and is now studying Latin. He has had some instruction in Algebra, but says he does not find it assist him in his calculations. He has not, it is said, been taught common Arithmetic regularly.

The performances of this wonderful lad are recorded. His methods are lucidly described by Faraday, so far as he had time to continue the trial of skill.

There is a note to Faraday from Davy:

Mr. Colburn, the father of the American boy who has such extraordinary powers of calculation, will explain to you the method his son used, in confidence. I wish to ascertain if it can be practically used.

H. DAVY.

On September 14, 1816, there is an entry referring to Priestley's experiments on mice "to ascertain the purity of different portions of the atmosphere, judging of it according to the time which those animals remained in it before dying." These experiments led to Priestley's Eudiometer. Into a tube,

Equal quantities of nitrous gas and the air to be tested were transferred in the water trough, and the diminution [in volume] of the mixture [was] noted. Dr. Priestley merely wrote down this diminution, and from that judged of the purity of the air. . . . Thus the first Eudiometer was formed in the year 1772.

He refers also to the work of Magellan, Fontana, Cavallo, Dalton (1802) and Pepys (1807).

He was sufficiently impressed by the truth of the next entry to give it a place:

Patriotism is the last refuge of a scoundrel.
                            Boswell's *Johnson.*

One of the curiosities is his

Receipt to make Gin:

Pearl ashes	$\frac{1}{4}$ lb.
Pot ashes	,,
Soper's lye water	3 quarts.
Oil of vitriol	1 oz.
Oil of almonds	1 pint.
Lime water	1 gallon.
Lump sugar	1 lb.
Spirits of wine	1 pint.
Turpentine	$\frac{1}{4}$ oz.

N.B. *Mix the oils with the spirits of wine to kill them.*
For the lime water. *8 lb. of unslaked lime, put it into a pail and pour on it 3 quarts of soft water: 1 hour, add three gallons and a quart of water: let it stand for 24 hours, clean it off and cork it up for use.*

He adds—

The above receipt and directions were given to me as correct, for the making of excellent gin. I suspect, nevertheless, that there is some mistake in the quantities; as of the Oil of Almonds.

He received many letters on table-turning and on spirit-rapping. In 1861 and 1864 attempts were made to obtain his consent to attend a meeting of spiritualists. He prescribed very rigid conditions. He refused the last invitation because he was so disappointed in the manifestations, and he wrote on October 8, 1864, to the Brothers Davenport—

If spirit communications not utterly worthless should happen to start into activity, I will trust the spirits to find out for themselves how they can move my attention. I am tired of them.

These entries sufficiently indicate the diversity of the subjects. Faraday reduced them to order by an ingenious system of indexing

... formed generally upon the principles recommended and practised by John Locke, Esq., author of An Essay on the Human Understanding.

The book is paged consecutively, and it contains an index having two narrow columns, followed by a third broad column. Into the first column are entered in their natural order the capital letters, spaced vertically about $1\frac{1}{2}$ inches apart. Into the second column are entered the vowels *a, e, i, o, u,* vertically, a set for each capital, so that the spacing is one-fifth that of the first. The third column is blank except for horizontal lines, ruled to separate the vowels; into this are entered in ink the pages corresponding to subjects. Thus "Nitrous Acid" is referred to on p. 132. The corresponding entry in the index is 132 on the third line, *i.e.* on the "i" line, of the "N" space. A long note on "Oratory" begins at p. 177. The corresponding entry in the index is 177 opposite to "a" of the "O" space.

CHAPTER XII

THE LABORATORY

LET us now follow him into his laboratory, for there he is most intimately in touch with the sources of his inspiration. Behold him—amidst the array of retorts, flasks, pumps, and crucibles, furnaces, bellows, carboys, bottles, gas holders, and blow-pipes, examining his store of reagents, his somewhat lavish supply of platinum foil and platinum wire, the book of gold-leaf and the hare's foot, the cocoon silk, the red sealing-wax made by himself, the stock of sand, coke, and charcoal, the carefully-checked weights, the finely-adjusted balances and, to his father's memory, probably the sledge and the anvil—a philosopher in gauze mask and leathern apron rippling with laughter over an experiment well done.

Examine next his treatise *Chemical Manipulation—being Instructions to Students of Chemistry on the Methods of Performing Experiments of Demonstration or Research with Accuracy and Success* and observe there something more of his environment and mode of operation. His notes on lighting, heating, and ventilation, the

THE CHEMICAL LABORATORY (LOOKING WEST), IN 1852.
FARADAY AT WORK.

From a water-colour painting by Miss Harriet Moore. Presented to the Royal
Institution by Miss Julia Moore, February 2nd, 1885.

construction of shelves, cupboards, sinks, furniture, and laboratory supplies are all of permanent value. They indicate how little he employed an instrument-maker when he could do things with his own hands, how much care he bestowed upon weighing and measuring, how skilled he was in delicate manipulation. Throughout his descriptions, observe too the extent to which, in the absence of modern refinements of apparatus, his fingers, thumbs, lips, and cheeks did service as corks, thermometers, and bellows. As a laboratory worker he was familiar with all the distinctions of terms, and in the performance of all the processes—lixiviation, deflagration, decantation, comminution, infusion, decoction, desiccation, sublimation, ignition, detonation, and incineration—he was a master. Glass-blowing, glass grinding, and other laboratory arts were constantly being improved by him. In the manipulation of glass tubes bent to serve special requirements, especially for distillation and sublimation, he was—as in everything else that he touched—expert. From paper and paste he improvised tubes that served many purposes better than glass or metal. Also he advocated the more general use of concentrated solar radiation as a means of applying intense heat in chemical experiments.

He realised that in their natural state and under normal conditions inert substances have comparatively little to tell us. His plan was to apply the forces of Nature to substances and thus to multiply the facts of science by every possible means. He worked upon the principle that nine-tenths of the facts of science have been wrung from Nature by artificial processes. To him the object of an experiment was two-fold: (1) To demonstrate; (2) to extend knowledge. He realised that skill derived from patient toil is necessary to enable a train of research to be carried further than its original object, to investigate collateral suggestions, to unite the links. In the laboratory, concentration for him demanded freedom from interruption. With regard to furniture: there might be a chair. In his own words:

A chair may be admitted, and one will be found quite sufficient for all necessary purposes, for a laboratory is no place for persons who are not engaged in the operations going on there.

There was wisdom also in his recommendation that purchases for the laboratory should be made "as necessity may arise," and he was obviously in favour of buying in the cheapest market. He says:

Hessian crucibles very far surpass the common English

THE CHEMICAL LABORATORY (LOOKING EAST) IN 1852.

From a water-colour painting by Miss Harriet Moore. Under the centre table is the great electro-magnet.

vessels in resistance of high temperatures and the action of fluxes. . . . The price is about 7d. for the nest of five or six crucibles. . . . Cornish crucibles are equally good with the Hessian crucibles.

In contrast with modern methods of high temperature measurement, his means were altogether inadequate, and he was severely hampered for lack of suitable equipment for that purpose. He complained of the deficiency, and he saw no likelihood that the want would soon be supplied. He added, however, that:

Of late years thermo-electric indications, founded on Seebeck's beautiful discovery, have been used to tell the temperature of furnaces; but, as yet, I believe, the direct application to the determination of the higher temperatures has not been made practical in the hands of an ordinary observer.

In his book on *Chemical Manipulation*, he includes electricity and magnetism—evidence this that although he found fame chiefly as a physicist, he was at heart a chemist. Here may be discerned the delicate tribute to Benjamin Franklin and to Volta, for already he distinguishes between "Franklinic" and "Voltaic" electricity. As a chemist he needed a static electrical machine or an electrophorous "to inflame combustible gaseous mixtures in the eudiometers," and he preferred conditions giving a decided luminous flash to those that gave a brush-discharge. In these experiments he heated his electrical machine by a sand-bath, or by warm air conducted to the machine by paper pipes from a crucible furnace.

With but few changes, his terminology has withstood the usage of a century. To him a "battery" was occasionally a group of Leyden jars, the arrangements of which, as he said, "belong principally to the electrician." He was there referring to the mode of connecting the jars in series or in parallel. The term "battery" was also used by him in its present sense to denote a group of voltaic cells.

It was as a chemist that he appreciated the advantages following upon the adoption of india-rubber for connecting retorts, condensers, and pipes. He was glad to see the rigid chemical apparatus of the time of Lavoisier, with its troublesome lutings and fractures, replaced by more flexible arrangements by the introduction of "elastic caoutchouc connectors."

He was not always an advocate of carrying out researches upon a grand scale—he even advised students to cultivate the habit of experimenting with small apparatus and on a minute scale. He

FARADAY'S SPECI-
MEN OF BENZINE.

From a photograph by
the Science Museum,
South Kensington.

FARADAY'S SPECIMENS OF RUSTLESS STEEL.

From a photograph by the Science Museum, South
Kensington.

FARADAY'S GREAT HORSE-SHOE
ELECTRO-MAGNET.

From a photograph by the Science
Museum, South Kensington.

assured them that it would be found highly valuable for the independence it gives to the philosopher
who may not be able to procure the larger, more
expensive, and scarcer instruments.

Above all he pleaded for method in research—
for method, that great source of facility and readi-
ness, equally influential in the performance of the
most common and the most difficult processes. To
this end, a convenient part of the laboratory tables
was to be set apart for experiments. It was not to be
encumbered; all the apparatus placed there by the
experimenter was to be regarded as sacred for the
time, nothing—not even an apparently dirty bottle
—was to be disturbed by other persons. Nevertheless,
the experimenter should, so far as possible, clear it
every evening. By the side of that sacred part was
to be another to be used as a side-board, so that the
experimenter might be disembarrassed of dirty
glasses, waste precipitates, and everything for which
he had no immediate use. All results worthy of
record were to be entered at the time of the experiment "whilst the things themselves are under the
eye, and can be re-examined if doubt or difficulties
arise." He deprecated the practice of delaying, as
it then becomes difficult to remember the succession
of events. Moreover, it was probable that some im-

portant point, that might suggest itself during the writing, could not subsequently be ascertained by reference to experiment. Date, temperature, and height of barometer, were in general to be noted. He gave useful hints for the preliminary examination of substances of unknown nature. In general, he recommended that the chemical solutions should be investigated before the precipitates—or in any case, that the investigator should select a scheme of methodical procedure and should adhere to it. New, important, and uncertain or unexpected results were to be repeated once or twice.

When carrying out a definite experiment, all the articles likely to be wanted were to be close at hand, so that the attention of the observer should not be diverted by the necessity of supplying some important omission. He advised students to exercise the greatest care in immediately labelling whatever is placed in reserve for future examination. Finally —here following Macquer, who had advocated this in the *Dictionnaire de Chimie*—he laid down general rules for cleanliness and order in the laboratory. He admitted how inconvenient it is to have to stop in the midst of researches to employ time in cleaning and arranging vessels and apparatus, but he knew it to be essential.

HANS CHRISTIAN OERSTED (1777-1851) AT THE AGE OF 26.
From an engraving by Chretien, in Paris, 1803.

CHAPTER XIII

ELECTRICITY FROM ORDINARY MAGNETISM

IT was his desire to leave on record, for "lovers of natural knowledge," a statement of the course of events relating to his experiments that linked electric-current phenomena with magnetism and with mechanical motion. The three volumes of his *Experimental Researches* contain evidence of this desire. They are augmented by his note-books and diaries. With these and other aids, it is possible to establish an approach to sequence between those events.

In 1791, the year that Faraday was born, Galvani —by experiments resembling somewhat those of Swammerdam, who in 1678 had observed muscular contractions resulting from silver-copper contacts—diverted the attention of physicists from static electrical phenomena. The idea of electricity as a current had next to take definite shape. Between 1796 and 1800, Volta extended the notion, and as Faraday afterwards said, "broke through the intellectual darkness." In 1819 or 1820 Oersted discovered, and on July 21, 1820, published an account of electro-magnetism as exemplified by the deflecting influence of an electric current upon a magnetic needle. This was quickly followed by the triumph of Ampère who, on September 18, 1820, presented his memoir and demonstrated that two electric currents in neighbouring wires exert mechanical forces upon each other. The laws established by Ampère, and his conception of a magnet as an assemblage of closed electric circuits each carrying a current, stimulated research to obtain mechanical rotations.

Faraday, in *Experimental Researches*, Vol. II, p. 159, remarks that:

Dr. Wollaston was, I believe, the person who first entertained the possibility of electro-magnetic rotation . . . it may have been about August, 1820, that Dr. Wollaston first conceived the possibility of making a wire in the voltaic circuit revolve on its own axis.

As a wire could not be made to revolve on its own axis, it is unnecessary to examine the baseless rumour that Faraday stole Dr. Wollaston's idea. It is more to the purpose to trace in what manner Faraday tried with success to rotate a suspended wire—in the voltaic circuit—round a magnet, and a magnet round such a wire. Reference ought to

ANDRÉ MARIE AMPÉRE (1775-1836).
From a portrait by David in 1829.

be made, however, to the work of Arago who, on September 25, 1820, communicated to the French

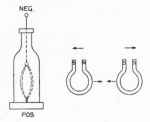

MAY 21, 1921. (SIR H. DAVY'S LECTURE).

"HORSE SHOE MAGNET (STRONG) APPROACHED TO THE SIDE OF THE ARC. THE ARC AND MAGNET MOVE IN CONTRARY DIRECTIONS, BUT THE COURSE OF THE ARC WAS CURVED THUS ⌒→ AND THUS ⌒→ WHEN THE MAGNET WAS TURNED ROUND, THEN THE ARC FOLLOWED ITS MOTIONS."

Fig. 16 (a)

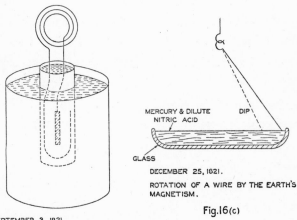

MERCURY & DILUTE NITRIC ACID   DIP

GLASS

DECEMBER 25, 1821.

ROTATION OF A WIRE BY THE EARTH'S MAGNETISM.

Fig.16(c)

SEPTEMBER 3, 1821.

CIRCULAR MOVEMENT OF A FLOATING WIRE CONVEYING A CURRENT.

Fig. 16(b)

Institute an account of experiments with a wire helix connected to a battery, whereby he magnetised iron and steel needles within the helix. This has to be distinguished from Arago's later experiments. Attention must also be directed to an entry in one of Faraday's diaries for May 21, 1821:

At the London Institution, Sir H. Davy's experiments on arc of voltaic flame in exhausted receiver.

2000 pairs of plates. Length of arc about 2.5 inches. Horse-shoe magnet (strong) approached to the side of the arc. The arc and magnet move in contrary directions, but the course of the arc was curved. . . . When the magnet was turned round, then the arc followed its motions. (Vide Fig. 16a.)

From the diaries, it further appears that from September 3, 1821, to September 8, 1821, Faraday was carrying out electro-magnetic experiments, using presumably a copper-zinc couple floated in dilute acid. The float supported in the air, above the acid, a vertical coil influenced by the magnet when the coil was connected to the couple (Fig. 16b).

There must next be noticed his entry of December 25, 1821:

Rotation of a wire by the earth's magnetism. In a large glass basin put mercury and a little dilute N.A. (nitric acid). Took about 6 inches of wire $\frac{1}{5}$th of inch thick, amalgamated. It formed a hook at the top by which it was suspended from another fixed hook as in tube apparatus. Put a little bit of [carbon?] on the lower end, the wire

FARADAY'S GREAT RING ELECTRO-MAGNET.
From a photograph by the Science Museum, South Kensington.

passing through it, and then held it over and on the mercury so that the wire formed an angle greater than the dip of the needle. Then connecting the mercury with one pole and the wire with the other, it began to rotate and continued rotating while the connection continued. On changing the connection, the direction of the motion changed also. (Fig. 16c.)

Gladstone says that on the occasion of the discovery in which a wire conveying a current was caused to move round a magnet, or a magnet round the wire, Faraday "danced about the revolving metals, his face beaming with joy . . . as he exclaimed, 'there they go! there they go! we have succeeded at last.'" After this discovery he proposed to his attendant a visit to the theatre, and gave him the option of which theatre it was to be. "Oh! let it be Astley's to see the horses." So to Astley's they went.

This success renewed his enthusiasm. To indicate that there were worthy competitors in the field, it suffices to refer to a letter from Ampère to him, dated January, 1822, now in the archives of the Institution of Electrical Engineers:

J'ai vu qu'un aimant tourne rapidement sur son axe quand flottant sur du mercure dans une situation verticale, au moyen d'un contrepoids de platine attaché à son extrémité inférieure. . . .

Faraday's diary for October, 1822, shows that he was taking account of Lubeck's thermo-electric experiment with a compound bar of antimony and brass wire:

The bar being heated at one end, the North pole of the magnet would go round it. . . .

For February 18, 1823, there are numerous draw-ings to illustrate "expected results in electro-magnetism—rotation of wire round magnet and magnet round wire." The entries continue to Janu-ary 22, 1823, and it must be inferred that he tried or intended to try all the arrangements of coils and magnets represented in his diagrams.

The scientific world was at that time thrilled with the possibilities of electro-magnetism; for on November 22, 1824, at the French Academy, Arago announced his discovery relating to magnet-ism and rotary motion, beginning with the obser-vation of the damping of oscillations of a magnetic needle when placed above and near to a conducting surface. Arago found that a circular copper plate revolving beneath the needle caused the needle to follow the motion. There was a demonstration of these phenomena in London on March 7, 1825.

Faraday was in pursuit, but he had not yet sur-

mounted his difficulties. His diary for December
28, 1824, records lack of success:

*Expected that an electro-magnetic current passing
through a wire would be affected by the approach of a
strong magnetic pole to the wire so as to indicate some
effect of reaction in other parts of the wire—but could not
perceive any effects of this kind. The power was from
2 to 30 pr [pairs] of 4-inch plates. The circuit was made
long, short, or moderate copper wire—or very fine silver
wire—the indicating needle was put into a galvanometer.
The pole was put into a helix, but in no case did the
magnet seem to affect the current so as to alter its intensity as shown upon a magnetic needle placed under a
distant part of it, although the magnetic pole was so
strong as to make the wire bend in its endeavours to pass
round it.*

He returned, as if for consolation, to chemistry,
on December 30, 1824. On November 28, 1825,
he renewed the attempt:

*Experiments on induction by connecting wire of voltaic
battery. A battery of 4 troughs, ten pairs of plates, each
arranged side by side. Experiment 1: The poles connected by a wire about 4 feet long, parallel to which was
another similar wire separated from it only by 2 thick-
nesses of paper—the ends of the latter wire attached to a
galvanometer exhibited no action. [He carried out at this
time three other experiments, but] could not in any way
render any inductions evident from the connecting wire.*

Meanwhile, on May 19, 1825, he discovered "a peculiar substance," benzine (Fig. 15c), which he describes as bicarburet of hydrogen. It was therefore well for chemistry and for the world's industries that his electro-magnetic experiments had not fully absorbed his attention. The note-books show that in February, 1828, he was at work upon the magnetis-ation of soft steel; on April 22, 1828, on experi-ments with magnets and copper rings; and on May 30, 1831, on another variation of his attack upon the riddle of rotation:

A silver wire ring (a) was so put into a vessel of water (b) that a part could project over the edge and be heated by a spirit flame (c) whilst a little magnetic needle (d) suspended by a long delicate silk fibre hung over the top. The ring was then moved in the direction of the arrows so that each part became hot by turns, then each (entered) suddenly in the water. No effect on the needle was observed, nor when the needle was perpendicular to the plane in which the wire moved. The experiment was made to ascertain whether as the heat travelled from particle to particle any electricity was put in motion.

This too was unsuccessful. The notes thereafter reveal him speeding on to investigations of amazing variety—upon meteoric stones, vibrations of plates, crispations, tuning forks and fluids, jelly, ripples, the effect of wind and water on a sandy shore, the formation of crystals, the manufacture of carbonic acid gas, and deposits from ancient temples. But ever faithful to his belief that he would find the long-sought answer to the electro-dynamic puzzle, he now concentrated all his resources, and victory came at last, with the entry on August 29, 1831:

Experiments on the production of Electricity from Magnetism, etc., etc.

Have had an iron ring made (soft iron), iron round and $\frac{7}{8}$th inches thick and ring 6 inches in external diameter. Wound many coils of copper wire round, one half the coils being separated by twine and calico—there were 3 lengths of wire each about 24 feet long and they could be connected as one length or used as separate lengths. By trial with a trough each was insulated from the other. Will call this side of the ring A. On the other side but separated by an interval was wound wire in two pieces together amounting to about 60 feet in length the direction being as with the former coils. This side call B.

Charged a battery of 10 pairs of plates 4 inches square. Made the coil on B side one coil and connected its extremities by a copper wire passing to a distance and just over a magnetic needle (3 feet from iron ring) then connected the ends of one of the pieces on A side with battery. Immediately a sensible effect on needle. It oscillated and settled at last in original position. On breaking connection of A side with battery, again a disturbance of the needle.

Made all the wires on A side one coil and sent current

Aug 29th 1831.

Facsimile page from Faraday's notebook recording his discovery
(August 29, 1831).

from battery through the whole. Effect on needle much stronger than before.

The effect on the needle then but a very small part of that which the wire communicating directly with the battery could produce.

William Whewell, who was Master of Trinity College, Cambridge, writing in 1857, associates the early chemical researches of Faraday with those of Davy and accentuates the importance of the Voltaic apparatus in initiating experiments. The decomposition of water, by Nicholson and Carlisle, in 1800, was declared by Davy to be "the true origin of all that has been done in electro-chemical science." Cruickshank followed by decomposing the muriates of magnesia, soda and ammonia, and made "the general observation that the alkaline matter always appeared at the *negative*, and the acid at the *positive* pole."

Upon his appointment, in 1801, to the Royal Institution, Davy came "into possession of a galvanic apparatus of great power." He repeated and extended the experiments of Nicholson and Carlisle, and he confirmed the view that chemical decomposition is consistent with the assumption that the elements are to each other *positive* and *negative*, respectively, *i.e.* that the elements appearing at the poles of the Voltaic apparatus are not generated *ab initio* but are liberated from the corresponding compounds. Whewell, however, informs us that this enunciation was, in 1802, rather conjectured than proved. Davy's capital experiment, "the decomposition of potassa into a metallic base and oxygen" and his decomposition of soda and of similar substances, were determining factors that concentrated the activities of the whole chemical world upon the investigation "in an intense degree." This work culminated in Davy's Memoir of 1806, which in the midst of war was crowned by the Institute of France.

Buonaparte had proposed a prize of sixty thousand francs to the person who by his experiments and discoveries should advance the knowledge of electricity and galvanism as much as Franklin and Volta did, and of three thousand francs for the best experiment which should be made in the course of each year on the galvanic fluid. The latter prize was, by the First Class of the Institute, awarded to Davy.

There is preserved in the Library of the Institution of Electrical Engineers, Faraday's own copy of "*Researches, Chemical and Philosophical chiefly concerning Nitrous Oxide, or Dephlogisticated Nitrous Air, and its Respiration. By Humphry Davy, Super-*

intendent of the Medical Pneumatic Institution, 1800."
This book was bound by Michael Faraday. It is
in the Introduction to this work that Davy wrote:

*The physical sciences are almost wholly dependent on
the minute observation and comparison of properties of
things not immediately obvious to the senses; and from the
difficulty of discovering every possible mode of examination, and from the modification of perceptions by the state
of feeling, it appears nearly impossible that all the relations of a series of phaenomena can be discovered by a
single investigation, particularly when these relations are
complicated, and many of the agents unknown. Fortunately for the active and progressive nature of the human
mind, even experimental research is only a method of
approximation to truth. . . . Early experience has taught
me the folly of hasty generalisation. We are ignorant of
the laws of corpuscular motion; and an immense mass of
minute observations concerning the more complicated
chemical changes must be collected probably, before we
shall be able to ascertain whether we are capable of discovering them. Chemistry in its present state is simply
a partial history of phaenomena, consisting of many series
more or less extensive of accurately connected facts.*

In the course of this series of experiments, Davy
subjected himself to a series of tests, in one of which
he says:

*I drank a bottle of wine in large draughts in less than
eight minutes. Whilst I was drinking, I perceived a sense*

of fulness in the head, and throbing of the arteries, not unanalogous to that produced in the first stage of nitrous oxide excitement. After I had finished the bottle, this fulness increased, the objects around me became dazzling, the power of distinct articulation was lost, and I was unable to walk steadily. At this moment the sensations were rather pleasurable than otherwise, the sense of fulness in the head soon, however, increased so as to become painful, and in less than an hour I sank into a state of insensibility. In this situation I must have remained for two hours or two hours and a half. I was awakened by headache and painful nausea.

He very wisely adds—

I ought to observe that my usual drink is water, that I had been little accustomed to take wine or spirits, and had never been compleatly intoxicated but once before in the course of my life. This will account for the powerful effects of a single bottle of wine.

Subsequently he inhaled a mixture of nitrous oxide and air, and he endeavoured to record his sensations throughout the ordeal. One collection of terms presented itself to his poisoned mind, and he exclaimed, with the most intense belief and prophetic manner:

Nothing exists but thoughts: the universe is composed of impressions, ideas, pleasures and pains.

The exceptional activity of men of science in Europe during the Napoleonic wars and during the revolutions that followed them was regarded as evidence that at such times human faculties attain nearest to the limit of their powers. Faraday's great discovery in 1831 may be regarded as the climax of these activities. In September of that year the British Association held their first meeting. They assembled at York. One of the many useful results that quickly followed was a Report by James F. W. Johnston upon Recent Progress and the Present State of Chemical Science, which was read subsequently at the Oxford meeting. From this it appears that at that time chemists were studying Combining Ratios—*i.e.* atomic weights. They had decided that all atomic weights are multiples of that of hydrogen, and they were examining the relationship of atomic weight to specific heat.

Weber had just determined specific heats by observing the change of elasticity and temperature of thin bars of metal when subjected to mechanical stress, using a method depending upon counting the vibrations of the bars in equal times before and after the extensions. His results confirmed the law of Dulong and Petit for iron, copper, silver, and platinum, *i.e.* that a given quantity of heat will raise by the same increment of temperature a portion of every solid body represented by its atomic weight. The application to gaseous bodies was not yet (1831) confirmed.

Meanwhile, Ampère and Dumas had taught that equal volumes of all gases, simple or compound, contain the same number of atoms; and the law of Boyle connecting volume and pressure had long been familiar to chemists. Bezelius, Liebig, Wohler, Prout, Dumas, and Mitscherlich were at work at these investigations. The elements were being usefully grouped, electro-positive metals were being separated from those that were electro-negative, and anomalies were being examined.

The diffusion of gases was under observation by Döbereiner, Magnus, Dalton, and Graham, and the properties of porous membranes had become widely known. Nieman repeated and confirmed Faraday's experiments on the condensation of gases. Davy was studying particularly combustion and flame. De Luc and others were ascertaining the temperature for maximum density of water, Leidenfrost and Perkins were obtaining remarkable experimental results concerning the spheroidal state of liquids, and Osann was investigating the properties of ice.

FARADAY'S INDUCTION COIL.
From a photograph by the Science Museum, South Kensington.

COMPOUND PERMANENT MAGNET USED BY FARADAY IN 1831.
From a photograph by the Science Museum, South Kensington.

Inorganic chemistry was also advancing—following upon the researches of Gay-Lussac, Thenard, Chevreul, and Faraday. Vegetable substances, especially food-stuffs and medicinal substances, were being analysed, and help in many directions was afforded by the optical work of Brewster.

The assemblage of steel bars (Fig. 18b), which is from a photograph by the Science Museum, South Kensington, is the original permanent magnet used by Faraday in 1831. It is described as a reconstruction of one made by Dr. Gowin Knight about the middle of the eighteenth century. This reconstructed magnet was the property of the Royal Society, and it "was in charge of Mr. Christie in 1831, when Faraday made use of it at his house. It consists of over 400 bars, each 15 inches long, 1 inch wide, and $\frac{1}{2}$-inch thick," and it weighs about 1000 lb. Faraday mounted a copper disc between the poles of this magnet, "and arranged two spring contacts, one pressing against the axis and one against the perimeter. On rotating the disc a steady electric current was obtained in a galvanometer connected to the two springs; and at that moment modern electrical engineering may be said to have been born." In 1845 he constructed the large horseshoe electro-magnet (Fig 15a).

It was discovered by Faraday (*Experimental Researches*, Vol. I, p . 9) in his experiments upon the "evolution of electricity from magnetism," that as an indication of the inductive effect between his helices "a minute *spark* could be perceived" when the contact of the battery with the primary helix was completed. The account of this experiment was read at the Royal Society on November 24, 1831. To obtain such sparks by other arrangements became thereafter a favourite theme or fashion in laboratories everywhere. In the *Philosophical Magazine* for June, 1832, Faraday expresses this by explaining that

In the race which Sig. Nobili and Antinori ran against me, they obtained the spark from the common magnet before me. . . . Mr. Forbes of Edinburgh first obtained the spark from a soft iron magnet made so by the influence of the natural loadstone. I was not aware of any other modes of performing the experiment except my original one.

It is appropriate next to refer to p. 403 of the *American Journal of Science*, Vol. XXII, for July, 1832, where, in an Appendix, Professor J. Henry contributed a note "On the Production of Sparks of Electricity from Magnetism." He had seen the announcement by Faraday that

When a piece of metal is moved in any direction in front of a magnetic pole electrical currents are developed in the metal, which pass in a direction at right angles to its own motion, and also that the application of this principle affords a complete and satisfactory explanation of the phenomena of magnetic rotation.

Professor Henry added:

No detail is given of the experiments, and it is somewhat surprising that results so interesting, and which certainly form a new era in the history of electricity and magnetism, should not have been more fully described before this time in some of the English publications; the only mention I have found of them is the following short account from the Annals of Philosophy *for April, under the head of Proceedings of the Royal Institution.*

This relates to a lecture given at the Royal Institution on February 17, 1832. Professor Henry then reproduces the report, and says that "before having any knowledge of the method given in the above account, I had succeeded in producing electrical effects in the following manner." He then describes his experiments with a coil and a galvanometer, illustrating "the reciprocal action of the two principles of electricity and magnetism." It is still more surprising that Professor Henry's own results were not earlier published. The date of them is not stated. The spark effects produced when "the opposite ends of the helices were held nearly in contact with each other, and the magnet suddenly excited," were recorded by Professor Henry, but he remarks:

It appears from the May No. of the Annals of Philo- sophy *that I have been anticipated in this experiment of drawing sparks from the magnet by Mr. James D. Forbes of Edinburgh, who obtained a spark (from a natural magnet) on the 30th of March; my experiments being made during the last two weeks in June . . . my result is entirely independent of his.*

Professor Henry notices the effect of using a long wire in such experiments. He recognised that the long wire becomes "charged with electricity which by its reaction on itself projects a spark when the connection is broken." The Journal also contains an account of "apparatus for producing the spark from a magnet according to the method of Nobili and of Faraday's wheel." This wheel was a copper disc rotating between the poles of a horseshoe magnet. A small circular portion of the disc near the centre, was amalgamated. The edge also was amalgamated. Contact with these amalgamated portions was made by copper plates to which wires were soldered. The wires led to a galvanometer.

In Faraday nature combined the proportion of

virility and sentiment that characterized the best English men and women of the Victorian age. While virility—used with perfect skill and judgment—exerted its full force against injustice, sentiment guarded the gates of friendship and kept him in touch with the world's needs. The extent to which community of interests in science could develop personal regard is exemplified by his correspondence with Schoenbein, between the years 1836 and 1862. After being edited by George W. A. Kahlbaum and Francis V. Darbishire, this correspondence was published in 1899. By graceful interchange, Miss Jane Barnard, Faraday's niece, had sent to Kahlbaum in 1897 the portion in her possession, for presentation to the University of Bâle; and a corresponding gift of the other portion was made by Schoenbein's daughters to the same University. The friendship between the two philosophers began on May 17, 1836, when Schoenbein, who was then professor of Chemistry at Bâle, wrote to Faraday as a complete stranger, to direct his attention to an observation:

If one of the ends of an iron wire be made red hot, and after cooling be immersed in nitric acid, spec. gr. 1.35, neither the end in question nor any other part of the wire will be affected, whilst the acid of the said strength is well known to act rather violently upon common iron. . . .

But by far the most curious fact observed by me is that any number of iron wires may be made indifferent to nitric acid by the following means. An iron wire with one of its ends oxidized is made to touch another common iron wire; both are then introduced into nitric acid of sp. gr. 1.35, so as to immerse the oxidized end of the one wire first into the one fluid, and to have part of both wires above the level of the acid. Under these circumstances no chemical action upon the wires will take place. . . .

These experiments at once aroused Faraday's spirit of inquiry, and in the course of the correspondence he soon realised that he had in Schoenbein an enlightened critic and an investigator worthy of attention. From the formal "yours very truly" of 1836, to the "ever truly yours" and "yours most sincerely" of 1837, the letters by 1841 developed at their terminals such phrases as "ever My dear Schoenbein, Yours affectionately, M . Faraday." And near the end, when the strength was failing and the memory was clouded, the radiance of this happy friendship glowed in his adieu: "I will not write any more. My love to you. Ever affectionately yours, M. Faraday."

Faraday's six lectures, delivered before "a juvenile auditory" at the Royal Institution during the Christmas holidays, 1859-1860 were published as a small book, edited by Sir William Crookes. This volume also contains the lecture delivered by Faraday at the Royal Institution on Friday, March 9, 1860, on "Lighthouse Illumination—the Electric Light." He showed his audience an electric arc, and he remarked:

This light is, in fact, produced by a forty-zinc power of burning; it is a power that I can carry about in my hands through these wires at pleasure, although if I applied it wrongly to myself it would destroy me in an instant, for it is a most intense thing, and the power you see here put forth while you count five is equivalent to the power of general thunderstorms, so great is its force.

His favourite topic for a juvenile audience, however, was undoubtedly the candle. He confessed:

I have taken this subject on a former occasion, and were it left to my own will I should prefer to repeat it almost every year, so abundant is the interest that attaches itself to the subject, so wonderful are the varieties of outlet which it offers into the various departments of philosophy.

CHAPTER XIV

NOTE-BOOKS AND DIARIES

LABORATORY details lacking in his printed papers can occasionally be supplied by examination of his original manuscript note-books and diaries now in the possession of the Royal Institution. These note-books and diaries are quite apart from the early note-books or commonplace books in the archives of the Institution of Electrical Engineers. So far as is known, there are at the Royal Institution ten manuscript books :

(i) In a green cover, bound by Faraday (about $8\frac{3}{4} \times 7\frac{3}{4}$ inches).

(ii) In a green cover, bound by Faraday (about $8\frac{1}{4} \times 6\frac{3}{4}$ inches).

(iii) In a mottled cover (about $9\frac{1}{4} \times 7\frac{3}{4}$ inches).

(iv) A set of seven volumes, about 13×8 inches, numbered 1 to 7 inclusively.

Book (i). Contains some of Faraday's suggestions for lectures 1827-1850. It begins thus:

I made Chemical Manipulation 12 lectures in the Spring of 1827 but found matter enough in the notes for at least 17. The notes of the six lectures given at the Royal Institution, Spring 1827, were sufficient for eleven lectures at least. . . . The eight lectures on the operations of the Laboratory at the Royal Institution, April 1820, were not to my mind. There does not appear to be that opportunity of fixing the attention of the audience by a single clear consistent and connected chain of reasoning which occurs when a principle or one particular application is made. The lectures appeared to me to be broken, or at least the facts brought forward were not used as proofs of their most striking or important effects, but as proof of some subordinate effect common to all. I do not think the operations of the laboratory can be rendered useful and popular in lectures at the same time, or at least I think I have not the way and can do better with other subjects. . . .

Then follows a list for proposed lectures as "Illus-trations of Chemical Principles Drawn from the Arts."

Book (ii). Green cover (1820 to Dec. 17, 1823). A "Note Book of things examined in Laboratory, Sept. 1820 to Dec. 17, 1823." The notes are con-tinued in (iii) until Nov. 14, 1832. The subjects dealt with are Artificial Camphor, Chloride of Carbon, Naphthaline and Chlorine, Sulphur, Ether and Chlorine, Vapour of mercury, gold, hydrogen, iodine, turpentine, earths, infusion of

M

bark. Then follows his description of the experiment (Fig. 16a) at Davy's lecture at the London
Institution, Finsbury Circus (May 21, 1821), on
the influence of a magnet upon an arc of voltaic
flame in an exhausted receiver. Other experiments
on electro-magnetic experiments follow. For example, he has an entry "Sept. 3, 1821, Electro-
magnetic expts. with Hare's Calorimoter," and he
proceeds to examine the motion of a conducting
wire round a magnetic pole. (The calorimotor is
mentioned on p. 157 of Vol. II of *Electrical Researches*. It appears to have been a cell of low resistance capable of heating wires, after the manner
of an earlier device of W. H. Pepys).

Book (iii). A continuation of (ii). It is a note-
book of things examined in the Laboratory from
Dec. 10, 1823, to Nov. 14, 1832. There are entries
on—Turpentine, Tamarind stones, Nitrous Oxide,
Sulphuric Acid, Alcohol, Steam, Steel, Atmosphere, Mercury, Sulphur, Water, fusion of steel and
nickel, balancing of gulls in the wind at Freshwater (Aug. 20, 1823), Ammonia, Crystal from
marsh at Woolwich, Electric powers of Oxalate of
Lime (dried in a Wedgwood basin) "when stirred
with a platina spatula it became strongly electrical,"
Coal Gas, Coal Tar distilled.

The remaining seven volumes are *Experimental Notes*, and are numbered and dated as follows:

No. 1. Feb.   2, 1831 to Apr.   6, 1832.
No. 2. Aug. 25, 1832 to Jan.   15, 1836.
No. 3. Jan.   15, 1836 to Nov.   5, 1838.
No. 4. Nov.   5, 1838 to Jan.   10, 1845.
No. 5. Jan.   10, 1845 to Jan.   21, 1850.
No. 6. Jan.   21, 1850 to Dec.   19, 1854.
No. 7. Mar.   3, 1855 to Mar.   6, 1860.

No. 7 is marked "Index, &c," but there is no index to these Notes, although there are a few pages of index-slips relating chiefly to galvanometers and to optics.

These seven volumes are for the most part em-bodied in *Faraday's Experimental Researches in Elec-tricity*, and they bear traces of having been used by him in preparing that account of his researches. As they begin somewhat earlier than *Experimental Researches*, however, and as they do not all appear in these printed volumes, they deserve close scrutiny. It is only possible here to give a hint of the contents, particularly of those of early date.

The greater part of the earlier diaries (i, ii, and iii) of Faraday is concerned with chemistry. His notes on electricity and magnetism sparkle out, in fact, in those early records amongst such matters as the examination of camphor, chlorine, chloride of carbon, naphthaline, iodine, turpentine, and caoutchouc—like diamonds scintillating in gold dust. When strung together, with the fewest possible explanatory additions in parenthesis, the most significant of the electrical and magnetic notes present themselves as in the above extracts from these diaries.

He continued the experiments on electro-magnetic induction as described in his *Experimental Researches*, and he asks the question:

May not these transient effects be connected with causes of difference between powers of metals in rest and in motion in Arago's experiments?

The diaries then proceed to deal with kindred matters, of which the following are examples:

Copper revolving plate. Dec. 5, 1831. *At Mr. Christie's again. Measurements of the Magnet. It belonged to Mr. Knight. It contains 437 bar magnets each 15 inches × 1 × ½ but it is not well arranged. Could get no sensible effect on a frog with the electricity from the whirling plate between the magnetic poles. . . .*

Dec. 8. *I have got my apparatus at home to act, and have been making precise observations upon the directions of the currents, etc., for in former notes there is much confusion from North end and North pole. (He then worked with a "marked" pole). "When the marked pole of the magnet entered the helix O as in figure, the marked end of the needle went* West. *Hence electrical currents as indicated by the arrows.*

Effect of withdrawal of magnet. *Helix approached to a magnet. Helix receded from a magnet. (These experiments with many modifications and extensions were continued until December 14, 1831).*

Effect of terrestrial magnetism in evolving electricity. *Obtained beautiful results (with a helix in the earth's field, with or without an iron core.) Made Arago's experiment with the earth magnet only (effect slight but distinct). Hence Arago's plate a new electrical machine.*

Dec. 23, 1831. *Experiments with battery (and helix) the spark never occurred except at the first moment of contact—nor afterwards though the battery contact continued. Important to decide whether electricity is evolved so long as wire moving or only whilst moving across magnetic curves of different intensity of power.*

Cylindrical magnet revolving in mercury. *Experiments with a single wire (loop in earth's field)— beautiful.*

January 10, 1832. *Experiments in the pond before Kensington Palace.*

March, 1832. *The lines or directions of force between 2 electrical conductors oppositely electrified may be called electric curves in analogy to magnetic curves. Do they not exist also in the electric current wire?*

The mutual relation of electricity, magnetism, and motion may be represented by three lines at right angles to each other, any one of which may represent any one of these points and the other two lines the other points.

June 11, 1832. *Have been experimenting on chemical power of magneto-electric current.*

Note-book No. 2. Aug. 25, 1832, to Jan. 1836. *Discharges of static electricity observed by galvanometer. Electrolysis.*

Aug. 30, 1832. *Discharge (quiet spark) through wet string. Discharge between charcoal surfaces (very bright). Effect of points on discharge. Amalgam on rubber of electrical machine.*

Current through jelly. (Nov. 1, 1832). *Experiments with ring electro-magnet, several windings on the same iron core. Thermo-electric experiments.*

Jan. 24, 1833. *Made some excellent experiments on ice (thermo-electric effects). Insulating power of ice. Insulating powers of gases, liquids, and solids.*

April 13, 1833. *Why did Davy require water in decomposing potassa? . . . May not non-conductors be decomposed by diminishing their insulating power until the electricity will pass. . . .?*

May 6, 1833. *Effect of electrified bodies on a polarised ray.*

Aug. 31, 1833. *Voltmeter with dilute sulphuric acid. The gas from the tubes after an experiment had a very strong electric smell, like brushes of a machine. . . .*

Sept. 16, 1833. If when iron becomes magnetic, electric currents are caused round its particles all parallel to each other—or if electric currents, before in all directions, are then put parallel—then there should be contraction of the iron in the direction of the magnetic axis, in consequence of the mutual attraction of these currents, and perhaps also expansions in directions perpendicular to these. (He observed momentary elongations of this kind, Sept. 16, 1833).

Movement of sap in trees (? electrical causes). Electro-chemical equivalents (Dec. 20, 1833).

Faraday himself says (*Experimental Researches in Electricity*, Vol. I, page 1):

Certain effects of the induction of electrical currents have already been recognised and described: as those of magnetization; Ampère's experiments of bringing a copper disc near to a flat spiral; his repetition with electro-magnets of Arago's extraordinary experiments, and perhaps a few others. Still it appeared unlikely that these could be all the effects which induction by currents could produce; especially as, upon dispensing with iron, almost the whole of them disappear, whilst yet an infinity of bodies, exhibiting definite phenomena of induction with electricity of tension, still remain to be acted upon by the induction of electricity in motion.

Further: Whether Ampère's beautiful theory were adopted, or any other, or whatever reservation were mentally made, still it appeared extraordinary, that as every

electric current was accompanied by a corresponding intensity of magnetic action at right angles to the current, good
conductors of electricity, when placed within the sphere
of this action, should not have any current induced
through them, or some sensible effect produced equivalent
in force to such a current.

These considerations, with their consequence, the hope
of obtaining electricity from ordinary magnetism, have
stimulated me at various times to investigate experimen-
tally the inductive effect of electric currents. I lately
arrived at positive results; and not only had my hopes fulfilled, but obtained a key which appeared to me to open
out a full explanation of Arago's magnetic phenomena,
and also to discover a new state, which may probably
have great influence in some of the most important effects
of electric currents.

These results I purpose describing, not as they were
obtained, but in such a manner as to give the most concise
view of the whole. . . .

About twenty-six feet of copper wire one-twentieth of
an inch in diameter were wound round a cylinder of wood
as a helix, the different spires of which were prevented
from touching by a thin interposed twine. This helix was
covered with calico, and then a second wire applied in the
same manner. In this way twelve helices were super-
posed, each containing an average length of wire of
twenty-seven feet, and all in the same direction. The
first, third, fifth, seventh, ninth, and eleventh of these
helices were connected at their extremities end to end, so
as to form one helix; the others were connected in a

similar manner; and thus two principal helices were produced, closely interposed, having the same direction, not touching anywhere, and each containing one hundred and fifty-five feet in length of wire.

One of these helices was connected with a galvano-meter, the other with a voltaic battery of ten pairs of plates four inches square, with double coppers and well charged; yet not the slightest sensible deflection of the galvanometer needle could be observed.

Undaunted, he proceeded to build a similar set of compound helices containing lengths of copper wire and lengths of soft iron wire respectively.

But whether the current from the trough was passed through the copper or the iron helix, no effect upon the other could be perceived at the galvanometer.

At last he tried two copper-wire helices, with a stronger battery.

When the contact was made, there was a sudden and very slight effect at the galvanometer, and there was also a similar slight effect when the contact with the battery was broken. But whilst the voltaic current was con-tinuing to pass through the one helix, no galvanometrical appearances nor any effect like induction upon the other helix could be perceived. . . . It was found in all cases that the induced current, produced by the first action of the inducting current, was in the contrary direction to the latter, but that the current produced by the cessation of the inducing current was in the same direction. For the purpose of avoiding periphrases, I propose to call this action of the current from the voltaic battery Volta-electric induction.

Thus, for more than five years, and possibly for ten, his mind was set upon deriving an electric current from a circuit under magnetic influences. He frequently tried and failed. So complete were those failures, so hopeless his repeated attempts, that in his ultimate success his persistency becomes the crowning glory of his philosophy. The failures arose from his expectation that induced currents could be obtained under steady-state conditions. Success came when those conditions were abandoned and transient effects were observed. The momentary currents—that evidenced themselves in a conductor when currents in neighbouring conductors were suddenly started—explained also Arago's results with the rotating disc; for, as Whewell admirably expressed it, "the momentary effect became permanent by the revolution of the plate."

Reference has been made to Faraday's advice to research workers that they should accustom themselves upon occasion to the use of small-scale apparatus. Although he achieved sometimes valuable results by experiments upon a small scale, he knew when to embark upon bigger projects. His tests upon the application of electric lighting to light-houses, in association with Trinity House, afford proof of this. He was also anxious to carry out full-scale experiments upon possible electro-magnetic currents derived from the earth's magnetism.

From his Note-book it is to be observed that :

On *January 10, 1832*, he experimented at "the pond before Kensington Palace." The Duke of Sussex had obtained leave from the King for these experiments to be made in the gardens, and he received all the help needed from the garden attendants.

A clean bright copper plate 2 feet by 1 foot had a thick copper wire soldered on at one corner. To this was made fast by clean metallic contact a copper wire $\frac{1}{20}$-inch thick and then the plate thrown into the water at the North East corner. . . . The wire was then continued round the Eastern side on the grass until it reached the South Eastern corner, where it was made fast to a similar plate as before, and that plate thrown in to water about 2 feet or 20 inches deep. . . . The plates were nearly 160 yards apart—the wire was of course much longer. The wire was then divided in the middle . . . (and connected to a galvanometer). At first I obtained deflections of the needle and these were very regular. . . . (But) on wash-

ing all the (mercury) cups and wires well in clean water, and using some of the same water to communicate equal temperatures to the two portions of mercury, and on holding the wires by paper handles, then obtained no effect and do not believe that under these circumstances any magneto-electric effects are produced, i.e. when wire and water have same (chemical) velocity of motion. It was wonderful to find the electric current from so small a cause as a little saline matter in one cup, or closer contact of the fingers on one wire ... but it showed also that the circuit was perfect and that the want of magneto-electric effects was not therefore due to any interrupting cause.

His description of how to make an electrophorus is not quite so precise as Volta's, for he does not point out the advantage of reducing the thickness of the dielectric. The material he adopts is equal parts of

> Common resin
> Shellac
> Venice turpentine

fused from 230° F. to 240° F. "until nearly all evolution of vapour has ceased, and the fluid is quiet." He forms it into a cake, one-third or one-half an inch in thickness, with tin-foil beneath. He used the electrophorous to "inflame" the explosive mixtures in eudiometers.

As a lute he recommends glazier's putty. For a "Cap Cement" he mixes

> 5 parts by weight of resin.
> 1 part of yellow bees'-wax.
> 1 part of Red Ochre or Venetian Red in fine powder.

He instructs us to dry the powder at 212° F. in an evaporating dish before mixing, to melt the wax and the resin together, and to stir in the powder by degrees, heating the whole just above 212° F. until all frothing ceases. The stirring is to be continued until the mixture is "quite cool."

He also used a Soft Cement, consisting of equal weights of yellow wax and turpentine melted together, with a little Venetian Red. He found this to be "superior for many purposes to hard cement." Powdered Gum was another of his favourite substances. As a Paste he used equal parts by weight of flour and powdered gum, and a small quantity of alum, mixed with water to a cream, and then heated and stirred until they boil, for a few minutes, care being taken to prevent evaporation.

CHAPTER XV

THE PRICE OF WISDOM

THE tenacity of purpose displayed in his researches is the more remarkable because of his breadth of view. Nature and life, in all their aspects, attracted him. Evidence of this is everywhere manifest. In August, 1823, he is found, for example, at Folkstone watching the sea-gulls, and endeavouring to comprehend how they sustain themselves as they glide against the wind without moving their wings. He asks:

How do these birds fly? And why may not a man or a machine fly in the same way in the same circumstances?

The next year, in the same month, from Freshwater Cliffs in the Isle of Wight, he again observes and notes the flight—a century in advance of the answer to his riddle.

To indicate his desire to advance the cause of fellowship between the leaders of literature, science, and art, there must be recorded his association with the inception of The Athenaeum. In 1823, the Right Honourable John Wilson Croker, who was

THE ATHENAEUM.
From a snapshot by the Author, September, 1930.

Secretary to the Admiralty, proposed to Sir Humphry Davy the formation of "a club for literary and scientific men and followers of the fine arts." From the account of the matter written by Henry R. Tedder, it appears that the Club was founded on February 16, 1824, at a meeting held in the apartments of the Royal Society at Somerset House. The name first adopted was The Society, but it was afterwards changed to The Athenaeum. It was instituted "for the association of individuals known for their scientific or literary attainments, artists of eminence in any class of the fine arts, and noblemen and gentlemen distinguished as liberal patrons of science, literature, or the arts. Gentlemen belonging to any of the classes before mentioned and desirous of joining the Club were invited to write to Mr. Faraday, Royal Institution," who had undertaken to act as temporary secretary. According to Tedder, the earliest minutes of the Club are in the handwriting of Faraday, but owing to the pressure of his scientific work, Faraday was soon obliged to relinquish the duties.

The present club-house of the Athenaeum (Fig. 19), which was designed by Decimus Burton, was built in 1829, and was opened on February 8, 1830. While it was being built, the members used a temporary club house at the South West corner of Regent Street. The first meetings of the members were held, however, in the rooms of the Royal Institution.

With a similar intent to aid a good cause, he consented in 1864 to be appointed a Vice-President of "The Albert Memorial Hall."

Faraday's knowledge was at the disposal of his country, and for this reason occasionally he was the victim of ignorance. Thus in April, 1825, it appears from his note-book that he received from the Woolwich authorities a crystal which he was told had been taken out of a piece of chalk. He tested it, and reported thus:

Specimen is a piece of Borax. Has not come from the chalk, but has either accidentally been supposed to do so, or has been mischievously described as having such a source, with intent to deceive.

Sometimes, also, he was called upon by the Law Courts to express his opinion as an expert chemist. An instance of this occurred in June, 1830, when a publican was charged before the Board of Excise with adulterating beer. Faraday reported that he had analysed it and discovered in it sulphate of iron, sodium chloride, and other foreign matters. The publican was fined £70.

Faraday, who began in poverty might have ended in affluence. He decided that his duty was to adhere to his scientific work at the Royal Institution, with the result that he was never a rich man. Instructive light is thrown upon this in a report written in 1862 by the Honorary Secretary, at that time, of the Royal Institution. He refers to a lecture given on March 3, 1810, by Sir Humphry Davy, who then explained that the first plan (in 1799) of the Royal Institution was that it should be a school for promulgating the knowledge and use of important mechanical inventions, and for connecting the views of men of science with those of artisans. The primary object was to exhibit working mechanical models, and generally to promote experimental science.

In 1799 Dr. Thomas Garnett took over the lectureship in experimental philosophy, mechanics, and chemistry at £300 a year, with residential apartments. At that time there were no other lectures on those subjects given in London except in the medical schools. Two centuries before, however, *i.e.* in the year 1597, lectures on astronomy were given at Gresham College in the City of London. Moreover, in 1775 the Bakerian Lecture was established at the Royal Society. This, as the author of the report points out, did not amount to public instruction, for the Gresham Lectures were in Latin, and the Bakerian Lectures were for Fellows of the Royal Society.

In July, 1801, the learned Dr. Thomas Young was appointed Professor of the Royal Institution at £300 a year, with rooms. For this moderate sum he delivered in 1802 a course of thirty-one lectures on Natural Philosophy, and in 1803 he extended this to sixty lectures. Thus were the gates of scientific knowledge opened to the general public.

In February, 1801, Sir Humphry Davy was appointed Assistant Lecturer in Chemistry, and Assistant Director of the Laboratory at £105, with one room, coals and candles. The next year he became Professor of Chemistry at £200. In 1803 this was increased to £300 a year. In 1805, when he was appointed Director of the Laboratory, he received a total of £400 a year. In 1813, a year after his marriage, Sir Humphry Davy resigned and was made Honorary Professor of Chemistry. This resignation was a heavy loss to science. The evidence is not sufficient to indicate the extent to which it was due to inadequate emoluments.

In 1813 Faraday was appointed Assistant in the Laboratory at 25s. a week, with two rooms. In

1816 his salary was raised to £100 a year. Even in 1825, when he was appointed Director of the Laboratory, there was no increase in that amount. In 1836, he was appointed Scientific Adviser to Trinity House at the nominal salary of £200 a year. He retained this appointment for 30 years. The public benefactor, Mr. Fuller, in 1833 endowed a Professorship of Chemistry at the Royal Institution, with £3333, and he appointed Mr. Faraday to the Chair "without calling upon him for lecture duty." This gave Faraday another £100 a year, *i.e.* £200 in all. It was not until 1853, when he was appointed Superintendent of the House and Director of the Laboratory, that he received £300 a year from the Royal Institution.

Faraday attracted large audiences, and his contributions to science, which began in 1816 and continued for nearly half a century, brought to the Institution great prestige. With truth the Honorary Secretary declared :

He has worked (1862) long and much for the love of the Institution, and little for its money. For 40 years, from 1813 to 1853, his fixed income from the Institution was not more than £200 per annum.

By universal consent, the discoveries, the skill, and the teaching of Faraday establish him amongst the immortals. This account of him can do no more than confirm what the facts of the last half century have revealed. In every direction of the advance of natural science and engineering his work and his name are manifest. Amidst activities and experiences calling for the utmost watchfulness and with the alternative paths to wealth, to ease, and to social distinction enticingly open to him, he held fast to the helm of conduct and he steered true to precepts and to conscience. For him the price of wisdom was above rubies. In a word, he was faithful to his own exalted philosophy, in accordance with which the Truth continues

In thoughts sublime that pierce the night like stars
And with their mild persistence urge man's search
To vaster issues.

ROLLO APPLEYARD.

INDEX

tureship at the Royal Military Academy, Woolwich (1829), 52; his mode of life and amusements, 52-55; his first appearance as Fullerian Professor of Chemistry (1833), 139, 195; suffers from fatigue and rheumatism, and makes a tour in Switzerland (1835), 55; granted a state pension (1835), 57-61; his poverty as a youth, 59; failing health and loss of memory (1837-40), 62; takes a second trip to Switzerland, 62; does a little work for Trinity House and begins his Christmas Juvenile Lectures at the Royal Institution, 62; investigates the Haswell Colliery disaster (1844), 63; from youth he had been a student of evidence, 64; improvement in his health (1845), 65; on his doctors' advice he gave up work, but later on resumed his researches (1849), 66; experiments on the submarine cable, 66; gives evidence before Public Schools Commission (1862), 76-81; his death (1867), 67; his mind and methods of investigation, 82-103; his remarkable onomastic power, 96; correspondence on scientific subjects, 104-128; his public services, 128-136; commonplace books, 137-145; his laboratory, 146-

152; his experiments on obtaining electricity from ordinary magnetism, 156-163, 170, 171, 184; Faraday's wheel, 172; his notebook sand diaries, 176-189; the price of his wisdom, 190-196

Faraday, Richard, 2, 9, 11
— Robert (grandfather of Michael), 2, 3, 9-12
— Robert (brother of Michael), 5, 14
— Robert (uncle of Michael), 11, 12
— *née* Barnard, Sarah, 41
— Thomas, 9
— Thomas (uncle of Michael), 11, 12
— William, 12
Fellowes, Sir Charles, 73
Field of force, 90
Flight, Faraday and, 190
Forbes, James D., 113, 170, 172
Force—Maxwell's definition of 111; *see also* Field of force; Lines of force
Fox, Lady Mary, 59, 60
Franklin, Benjamin, 95, 149, 164
French revolution, 17
Fullerian Professorship of Chemistry, 139, 195

Galvani, Luigi, 153
Garcia, Manuel, 52
Garnett, Dr. Thomas, 193
Gases, researches in, 168
Gassiot, John, 127
Gauss, Chas. Fred., 119, 125
Geissler, Mr., 122
German schoolmaster's list of punishments, 141

PRINTED IN GREAT BRITAIN BY ROBERT MACLEHOSE AND CO. LTD
THE UNIVERSITY PRESS, GLASGOW

2/6